my **revisi⊙n** notes

AQA AS/A-level Year 1
CHEMISTRY

Rob King

HODDER
EDUCATION
AN HACHETTE UK COMPANY

Hachette UK's policy is to use papers that are natural, renewable and recyclable products and made from wood grown in sustainable forests. The logging and manufacturing processes are expected to conform to the environmental regulations of the country of origin.

Orders: please contact Bookpoint Ltd, 130 Park Drive, Milton Park, Abingdon, Oxon OX14 4SB. Telephone: (44) 01235 827720. Fax: (44) 01235 400454. Email education@bookpoint.co.uk

Lines are open from 9 a.m. to 5 p.m., Monday to Saturday, with a 24-hour message answering service. You can also order through our website: www.hoddereducation.co.uk

ISBN: 978 1 4718 4205 4

First published in 2015 by

Hodder Education,
An Hachette UK Company
Carmelite House
50 Victoria Embankment
London EC4Y 0DZ

www.hoddereducation.co.uk

Impression number   10 9 8 7 6 5 4 3 2 1

Year   2019 2018 2017 2016 2015

Cover photo reproduced by permission of SSilver/Fotolia

Typeset by Integra Software Services Pvt. Ltd., Pondicherry, India

Printed in Spain

A catalogue record for this title is available from the British Library.

Get the most from this book

Everyone has to decide his or her own revision strategy, but it is essential to review your work, learn it and test your understanding. *My Revision Notes* will help you to do that in a planned way, topic by topic. Use this book as the cornerstone of your revision and don't hesitate to write in it — personalise your notes and check your progress by ticking off each section as you revise.

Tick to track your progress

Use the revision planner on pages 4 and 5 to plan your revision, topic by topic. Tick each box when you have:
- revised and understood a topic
- tested yourself
- practised the exam questions and gone online to check your answers and complete the quick quizzes

You can also keep track of your revision by ticking off each topic heading in the book. You may find it helpful to add your own notes as you work through each topic.

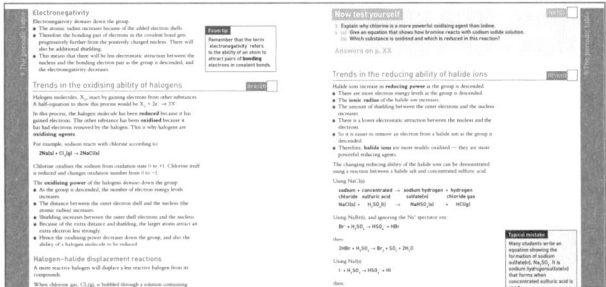

Features to help you succeed

Exam tips and summaries

Throughout the book there are tips from examiners to help you boost your final grade. Summaries provide advice on how to approach each topic in the exams, and suggest other things you might want to mention to gain those valuable extra marks.

Typical mistakes

Examiners identify the typical mistakes students make and explain how you can avoid them.

Now test yourself

These short, knowledge-based questions provide the first step in testing your learning. Answers are at the back of the book.

Definitions and key words

Clear, concise definitions of essential key terms are provided where they first appear.

Key words from the specification are highlighted in bold throughout the book.

Revision activities

These activities will help you to understand each topic in an interactive way.

Exam practice

Practice exam questions are provided for each topic. Use them to consolidate your revision and practise your exam skills.

Online

Go online to check your answers to the exam questions and try out the extra quick quizzes at **www.hoddereducation.co.uk/myrevisionnotes**

My revision planner

Physical chemistry

REVISED TESTED EXAM READY

Exam practice answers and quick quizzes at **www.hoddereducation.co.uk/myrevisionnotes**

Inorganic chemistry

Organic chemistry

REVISED   TESTED   EXAM READY

Exam practice answers and quick quizzes at
www.hoddereducation.co.uk/myrevisionnotes

Countdown to my exams

6–8 weeks to go

- Start by looking at the specification — make sure you know exactly what material you need to revise and the style of the examination. Use the revision planner on pages 4 and 5 to familiarise yourself with the topics.
- Organise your notes, making sure you have covered everything on the specification. The revision planner will help you to group your notes into topics.
- Work out a realistic revision plan that will allow you time for relaxation. Set aside days and times for all the subjects that you need to study, and stick to your timetable.
- Set yourself sensible targets. Break your revision down into focused sessions of around 40 minutes, divided by breaks. These *Revision Notes* organise the basic facts into short, memorable sections to make revising easier.

REVISED ☐

2–5 weeks to go

- Read through the relevant sections of this book and refer to the exam tips, summaries, typical mistakes and key terms. Tick off the topics as you feel confident about them. Highlight those topics you find difficult and look at them again in detail.
- Test your understanding of each topic by working through the 'Now test yourself' questions in the book. Look up the answers at the back of the book.
- Make a note of any problem areas as you revise, and ask your teacher to go over these in class.
- Look at past papers. They are one of the best ways to revise and practise your exam skills. Write or prepare planned answers to the exam practice questions provided in this book. Check your answers online and try out the extra quick quizzes at **www.hoddereducation.co.uk/myrevisionnotes**
- Use the revision activities to try out different revision methods. For example, you can make notes using mind maps, spider diagrams or flash cards.
- Track your progress using the revision planner and give yourself a reward when you have achieved your target.

REVISED ☐

One week to go

- Try to fit in at least one more timed practice of an entire past paper and seek feedback from your teacher, comparing your work closely with the mark scheme.
- Check the revision planner to make sure you haven't missed out any topics. Brush up on any areas of difficulty by talking them over with a friend or getting help from your teacher.
- Attend any revision classes put on by your teacher. Remember, he or she is an expert at preparing people for examinations.

REVISED ☐

The day before the examination

- Flick through these *Revision Notes* for useful reminders, for example the exam tips, summaries, typical mistakes and key terms.
- Check the time and place of your examination.
- Make sure you have everything you need — extra pens and pencils, tissues, a watch, bottled water, sweets.
- Allow some time to relax and have an early night to ensure you are fresh and alert for the examinations.

REVISED ☐

My exams

AS Chemistry Paper 1

Date:...

Time:...

Location:...

AS Chemistry Paper 2

Date:...

Time:...

Location:...

1 Atomic structure

The structure of atoms

Protons, neutrons and electrons

Table 1.1 Fundamental particles

Particle	Relative charge	Relative mass
Proton	+1	1
Neutron	0	1
Electron	−1	$\dfrac{1}{1836}$

The **atomic number** (Z) and **mass number** (A) can be used to deduce the number of protons, neutrons and electrons in any atom or ion.

To calculate the number of neutrons in the nucleus, the atomic number (equal to the number of protons) is subtracted from the mass number (equal to the number of protons + neutrons).

For example, the elements of calcium, potassium and phosphorus are represented as:

$$^{40}_{20}\text{Ca} \qquad ^{39}_{19}\text{K} \qquad ^{31}_{15}\text{P}$$

Atoms do not have an overall charge because the number of positively charged protons is the same as the number of negatively charged electrons. However, when an **ion** forms — either by losing or by gaining electrons — there is an overall charge because there will be an unequal number of positive charges and negative charges.

> **Atomic number** is the number of protons in the nucleus of an atom (or ion).
>
> **Mass number** is the total number of protons plus neutrons in the nucleus.

> **Exam tip**
>
> Remember that when atoms lose electrons they form positively charged ions; when atoms gain electrons they form negatively charged ions.

Isotopes

Many elements exist as **isotopes**. In a sample of chlorine, for example, 75% of the chlorine atoms have a mass number of 35 and 25% have a mass number of 37. These atoms have different masses because they have different numbers of neutrons.

In Table 1.2, the numbers of protons, neutrons and electrons are indicated for all three isotopes of magnesium, thus showing the differing numbers of neutrons.

> **Isotopes** are atoms with the same number of protons, but different numbers of neutrons.

Table 1.2 The isotopes of magnesium (atomic number = 12)

Isotopes	Protons	Neutrons	Electrons
^{24}Mg	12	12	12
^{25}Mg	12	13	12
^{26}Mg	12	14	12

Mass spectrometry

The mass spectrometer

The **time of flight (TOF) mass spectrometer** (Figure 1.1) is a device that enables substances (elements or compounds) to be analysed by determining the masses of ions formed.

Figure 1.1 Diagram of a mass spectrometer

There are four stages involved in analysing a sample:

1 **Electron spray ionisation** — a high-energy beam of electrons from the electron gun removes the highest-energy (outer) electron from a molecule or an atom, forming a positively charged ion. For example, using gallium:

$$Ga(g) \rightarrow Ga^+(g) + e^-$$

2 **Acceleration** — the positively charged ion is accelerated towards a negatively charged electrode. This provides all ions with the same kinetic energy.
3 **Ion drift** — the positively charged ions are electrostatically attracted to the negatively charged cathode.
4 **Ion detection and data analysis** — ions of different masses are detected electronically and produce a small, varying electrical current that can be amplified and displayed on a computer. A mass spectrum is produced.

> **Exam tip**
>
> Equations showing ionisation processes that take place in a mass spectrometer occur in the gas phase, so make sure that state symbols are added to equations showing ionisations.

> **Revision activity**
>
> Try to make up an acronym that will help you to remember the main processes involved when analysing a sample in a mass spectrometer.

How to interpret a mass spectrum

The mass spectrum of lead is shown in Figure 1.2.

Figure 1.2 The mass spectrum of lead

Exam practice answers and quick quizzes at **www.hoddereducation.co.uk/myrevisionnotes**

- In the spectrum there are four peaks. This means that there are four isotopes of lead in the sample: ^{204}Pb, ^{206}Pb, ^{207}Pb and ^{208}Pb.
- There is more ^{208}Pb than any other lead isotopes because this is the tallest peak — this isotope gives the peak with the highest abundance.
- You can calculate a value for the **relative atomic mass** (A_r) of lead by multiplying each mass number by its abundance percentage (divided by 100) and then adding them all together. If the abundances in this case are ^{204}Pb (4.9%), ^{206}Pb (23.2%), ^{207}Pb (19.2%) and ^{208}Pb (52.7%), the calculation will be:

$$A_r \text{ for lead} = \left(\frac{4.9}{100} \times 204\right) + \left(\frac{23.2}{100} \times 206\right) + \left(\frac{19.2}{100} \times 207\right) + \left(\frac{52.7}{100} \times 208\right)$$

$$= 207.1 \text{ (no units)}$$

Mass spectrometers allow **relative molecular masses** and their abundances to be determined with a high degree of precision.

Mass spectrometers can be used in planetary space probes to analyse samples of material found on other planets, and this information can then be beamed to Earth. This way the elements can be determined, together with the identity of molecules.

Now test yourself

TESTED ☐

1 Deduce the number of protons, neutrons and electrons in each of:
 (a) $^{19}_{9}$F
 (b) $^{74}_{34}$Se
 (c) $^{48}_{22}$Ti^{2+}
 (d) $^{79}_{35}$Br$^-$

2 Calculate the relative atomic mass for a sample of krypton from the data in Table 1.3. Give your answer to 2 decimal places.

Table 1.3

Isotopes	$^{78}_{36}$Kr	$^{80}_{36}$Kr	$^{82}_{36}$Kr	$^{83}_{36}$Kr	$^{84}_{36}$Kr	$^{86}_{36}$Kr
% abundance	0.35	2.3	11.6	11.5	56.9	17.4

3 A sample of boron is found to have a relative atomic mass of 10.8. Assuming that there are only two isotopes of this element, ^{10}B and ^{11}B, determine the percentage of each isotope in the sample.

Answers on p. 100

Exam tip

In a mass spectrum, mass-to-charge ratio is measured on the horizontal axis and relative abundance is measured on the vertical axis. The charge of an ion is normally designed to be +1. In a few cases, a +2 ion may form when a second electron is removed.

Revision activity

Look up on the internet an element of your choice and find out about the relative abundances of its isotopes. Then work out the element's relative atomic mass to practice this type of calculation.

Relative atomic mass (A_r) is the weighted mean mass of an atom compared with $\frac{1}{12}$ the mass of an atom of ^{12}C. ^{12}C has the value of 12.0000 on this scale.

Relative molecular mass (M_r) is the weighted mean mass of a molecule compared with $\frac{1}{12}$ the mass of an atom of ^{12}C. It is the sum of the relative atomic masses of the atoms in a molecule.

Electron configuration

Electrons occupy **energy levels** (or shells) when orbiting an atomic nucleus. Energy levels are made up of **sublevels**, or subshells.

Sublevels fill up in the order shown in Figure 1.3, lowest energy first.

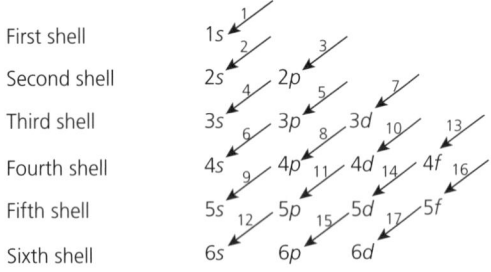

Figure 1.3 Arrangement of sublevels

> **Exam tip**
>
> **Sublevels** are made up of **orbitals** and one orbital of any type can only hold up to two electrons.

You can write an electronic configuration for an atom or an ion by putting the correct number of electrons into each sublevel: 2 electrons in an s-sublevel; 6 electrons in a p-sublevel; 10 electrons in a d-sublevel and 14 in an f-sublevel. The number of electrons in a shell is given by $2n^2$, where n is the number of the shell. For example, in the third shell $n = 3$, so the number of electrons is 2×3^2, which is 18. Table 1.4 gives some examples.

Table 1.4 Some electron configurations

Element	Symbol/ion	Atomic number	Electronic configuration
Sodium	Na	11	$1s^2, 2s^2, 2p^6, 3s^1$
	Na$^+$		$1s^2, 2s^2, 2p^6$
Potassium	K	19	$1s^2, 2s^2, 2p^6, 3s^2, 3p^6, 4s^1$
	K$^+$		$1s^2, 2s^2, 2p^6, 3s^2, 3p^6$
Sulfur	S	16	$1s^2, 2s^2, 2p^6, 3s^2, 3p^4$
	S^{2-}		$1s^2, 2s^2, 2p^6, 3s^2, 3p^6$
Gallium	Ga	31	$1s^2, 2s^2, 2p^6, 3s^2, 3p^6, 4s^2, 3d^{10}, 4p^1$
	Ga^{3+}		$1s^2, 2s^2, 2p^6, 3s^2, 3p^6, 3d^{10}$
Krypton	Kr	36	$1s^2, 2s^2, 2p^6, 3s^2, 3p^6, 4s^2, 3d^{10}, 4p^6$

> **Exam tip**
>
> Notice that the $4s$-sublevel fills up before the $3d$-sublevel; this means that the 4th energy level starts to fill up before the 3rd energy level has been filled completely.

Now test yourself

TESTED

4 (a) Beryllium ($Z = 4$), magnesium ($Z = 12$) and calcium ($Z = 20$) are the first three members of group 2 of the periodic table. Write out each element's electronic configuration.

(b) An ion of charge +3 has the electronic configuration $1s^2, 2s^2, 2p^6$. What is the atomic number, Z, for the ion?

Answers on p. 100

Ionisation energies

First ionisation energy

The equation to represent the **first ionisation energy** of calcium is:

$$Ca(g) \rightarrow Ca^+(g) + e^-$$

A plot of first ionisation energy against atomic number is shown in Figure 1.4. This graph can provide valuable evidence for the electron arrangement in levels.

> **First ionisation energy** is defined as the energy required to remove 1 mol of electrons from 1 mol of gaseous atoms under standard conditions (298 K and a pressure of 100 kPa).

Figure 1.4 First ionisation energy graph

Energy levels

It is possible to remove more than one electron from an atom if the energy of the bombarding electrons is sufficient. For example, the third ionisation energy of argon is represented as:

$$Ar^{2+}(g) \rightarrow Ar^{3+}(g) + e^-$$

Successive ionisation energies for elements give valuable evidence about the existence of energy levels.

Figure 1.5 Graph of $\log_{10}$(ionisation energy) versus number of the electron being removed for oxygen

From Figure 1.5 it can be seen that:
- there is a large jump in ionisation energy required moving from the sixth to the seventh electron removal
- six electrons are relatively easy to remove from the nucleus, whereas two electrons are a lot more difficult to remove

The explanation is that the eight electrons must exist in two separate energy levels — two electrons are in an energy level closest to the positive charge of the nucleus and are therefore harder to remove. The other six electrons are in a higher energy level further from the nucleus and are therefore easier to remove.

Now test yourself

TESTED

5 (a) Sketch a graph to show the successive ionisation energies for silicon, $Z = 14$.
  (b) Write an equation to show the fourth ionisation energy of phosphorus, P.

Answer on p. 100

Evidence for energy levels

Variation of first ionisation energies down group 2 (Be–Ba)

The trend in first ionisation energies is a decrease in the energy on moving down the group.

The explanation is as follows:
- Despite the increased nuclear charge, the electron being removed is in a new energy level which is progressively further from the nucleus.
- The extra energy level provides extra shielding for the removed electron from the attraction of the positively charged nucleus.
- The net effect is to decrease the ionisation energy.

Evidence for energy sublevels

Variation of first ionisation energies across period 3 from left to right

The trend in first ionisation energies is a general increase across period 3 from sodium to argon.

The explanation is as follows:
- The electrons are being removed from the same electron energy level.
- The nuclear charge is increasing as more protons are being added from left to right.
- The electrons experience a greater attraction as the atom increases in atomic number.

Although the general trend is for ionisation energy to increase from left to right across a period, there are two small decreases.

From group 2 to group 3: magnesium to aluminium

The explanation for the decrease is as follows:
- Despite the increased nuclear charge, the added electron is in a new p-sublevel of slightly higher energy, and this is slightly further from the nucleus.
- The s^2 electrons, for the group 3 element, provide some shielding.
- The overall effect is for the ionisation energy to decrease.

From group 5 to group 6, phosphorus to sulfur

The explanation for the decrease is as follows:

● Despite the increased nuclear charge, the electron from the group 6 element is being removed from a p^4 configuration (Figure 1.6).

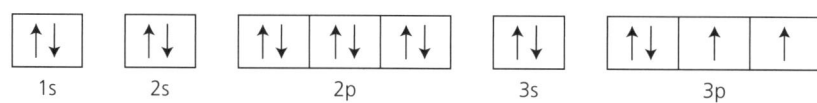

1s   2s   2p   3s   3p

Figure 1.6 Arrangement of electrons in orbitals for sulfur

● There are four electrons in the outer a p-sublevel, so two of these must be paired in one orbital.
● This electron–electron repulsion lowers the attraction between the fourth electron and the nucleus.
● So the electron is easier to remove.

Exam practice

1 (a) Write the electron configuration of an Al^+ ion. [1]
 (b) (i) State the meaning of the term 'first ionisation energy'. [2]
    (ii) Write an equation, including state symbols, to show the reaction that describes the second ionisation energy of aluminium. [2]
    (iii) Explain why the second ionisation energy of aluminium is higher than the first ionisation energy of aluminium. [2]
 (c) State and explain the general trend in the first ionisation energies of the period 3 elements sodium to chlorine. [3]
 (d) Explain why sulfur has a lower first ionisation energy than phosphorus. [2]
 (e) Explain why argon ($Z = 18$) has a much higher first ionisation energy than potassium ($Z = 19$) even though potassium has a larger positive nuclear charge. [2]

2 A sample of sulfur consisting of three isotopes has a relative atomic mass of 32.16. Table 1.5 gives the relative abundances of two of these isotopes.

Table 1.5

Mass number of isotope	32	33
Relative abundance/%	91.0	1.8

Use this information to determine the relative abundance and hence the mass number of the third isotope. Give your answer to the appropriate number of significant figures. [4]

3 Which of these atoms has the smallest number of neutrons? [1]
 A ^{3}H
 B ^{4}He
 C ^{5}He
 D ^{4}Li

Answers and quick quiz 1 online

ONLINE

Summary

You should now have an understanding of:
● the properties of protons, neutrons and electrons
● isotopes
● how a time of flight mass spectrometer works
● how a mass spectrum can be interpreted to provide information about isotopes

● how to calculate the relative atomic mass of an element using its mass spectrum
● electronic arrangement in terms of s, p, d notation
● ionisation energy
● the evidence for energy levels and sublevels from ionisation energies

2 Amount of substance

The mole and the Avogadro constant (L)

Definitions

The mass of **1 mole** of an element or compound is its relative atomic mass (A_r) or relative molecular mass (M_r) expressed in grams.

An **amount of substance** is measured in moles:

$$\text{number of mol} = \frac{\text{mass of substance in g}}{\text{mass of 1 mol of that substance}}$$

or:

$$\text{mass of substance} = \text{mass of 1 mol} \times \text{number of moles}$$

> **1 mole** is defined as the amount of substance that contains as many elementary particles as there are atoms in exactly 12 g of the ^{12}C isotope.
>
> The number 6×10^{23}, referred to as the **Avogadro constant**, is the number of specified particles — electrons, atoms, molecules or ions — in 1 mole.

Example

You are provided with a sample of 0.56 mol potassium dichromate(VI) ($K_2Cr_2O_7$). Calculate:
(a) the mass of the sample
(b) the number of potassium ions that would be present

Answer

(a) mass of 1 mol of $K_2Cr_2O_7$ = (2 × 39.0) + (2 × 52.0) + (7 × 16.0) = 294 g
   mass of substance = mass of 1 mol × number of mol
   0.56 mol will have a mass of 294 g × 0.56 = 164.64 g
(b) For every 1 mol of potassium dichromate(VI) ($K_2Cr_2O_7$) there are 2 mol of potassium ions. Therefore, 0.56 mol of potassium dichromate(VI) would contain 0.56 × 2 mol of potassium ions, that is, 1.12 mol.
   The number of particles in 1 mol is given by the Avogadro constant, 6×10^{23}, so the number of potassium ions present will be $1.12 \times 6 \times 10^{23}$, that is, 6.72×10^{23}.

> **Exam tip**
>
> Sometimes the term 'mol' is used to abbreviate the term 'moles', especially when it follows a number.

> **Exam tip**
>
> The first step is always to work out the mass of 1 mol. This is then *multiplied* by the number of moles to calculate a mass.

Empirical and molecular formulae

Definitions

The molecular formulae for ethane and hydrogen peroxide are C_2H_6 and H_2O_2 respectively, whereas the simplest whole-number ratios for these formulae — the empirical formula — are CH_3 and HO respectively.

> An **empirical formula** is a formula representing the simplest whole-number ratio of atoms of each element in a compound.
>
> A **molecular formula** represents the actual numbers of atoms of each element in one molecule.

Example 1

A hydrocarbon contains 2.51 g of carbon and 0.488 g of hydrogen. What is the empirical formula of the hydrocarbon?

Answer

mass of carbon = 2.51 g   mass of hydrogen = 0.488 g

Convert into moles by dividing by the A_r for each element:

$$\text{mol of C} = \frac{2.51}{12.0} \qquad \text{mol of H} = \frac{0.488}{1.0}$$

$$= 0.209 \, \text{mol} \qquad\qquad = 0.488 \, \text{mol}$$

Simplify the ratio by dividing each by the smaller number of moles:

$$\frac{0.209}{0.209} = 1 \qquad\qquad \frac{0.488}{0.209} = 2.33$$

Therefore, the ratio C : H is 1 : 2.33 or 3 : 7 (by multiplying each by 3 to get whole numbers). So the empirical formula is C_3H_7. If the relative molecular mass was given as 86 then the molecular formula would be C_6H_{14} since two 'lots' of the empirical formula would be required to give this molar mass.

Exam tip

Try to recognise certain ratios as being whole-number ratios in 'disguise', for example, 1 : 1.5 is 2 : 3; 1 : 1.33 is 3 : 4 and so on.

Questions featuring percentage compositions may also be set.

Example 2

A compound was found to contain 40.0% sulfur and 60.0% oxygen. What is the empirical formula for the compound? [A_r data: S = 32.1; O = 16.0]

Answer

If we assume the total mass of the compound is 100 g, then the masses of sulfur and oxygen will be 40.0 g and 60.0 g respectively.

mass of sulfur = 40.0 g   mass of oxygen = 60.0 g

Convert into moles:

$$\frac{40.0}{32.1} = 1.25 \, \text{moles} \qquad\qquad \frac{60.0}{16.0} = 3.75 \, \text{moles}$$

The ratio of sulfur to oxygen is 1.25 : 3.75 or 1 : 3, so the empirical formula of the compound is SO_3.

Exam tip

Remember to divide each amount in moles by the smallest value — this will normally give new numbers that are easier to recognise as a whole-number ratio.

Now test yourself

1 A compound is found to contain 1.00 g calcium and 1.77 g of chlorine only. What is its empirical formula? [A_r data: Ca = 40.1; Cl = 35.5]
2 A compound of calcium, silicon and oxygen is found to contain 0.210 g of calcium, 0.147 g of silicon and 0.252 g of oxygen. What is its empirical formula? [A_r data: Si = 28.1; Ca = 40.1; O = 16.0]
3 An oxide of nitrogen was found to contain 30.4% nitrogen by mass. The M_r of the oxide is 92.0. [A_r data: N = 14.0; O = 16.0]
   (a) What is the empirical formula of the oxide?
   (b) What is the molecular formula of the compound?
4 Caffeine is an organic molecule found in various natural products like coffee beans. Its displayed structure is shown in Figure 2.1.

Figure 2.1

(a) What is the molecular formula of a caffeine molecule?
(b) A sample of coffee was analysed and found to contain 5.60×10^{-3} g of caffeine.
   (i) How many molecules of caffeine would this mass represent?
   (ii) The sample is then combusted in excess oxygen. What is the maximum number of carbon dioxide molecules that could be produced in the combustion?
   [A_r data: N = 14.0; C = 12.0; O = 16.0; H = 1.0]

Answers on p. 100

The ideal gas equation

Calculations

This states that:

$$pV = nRT$$

where p is the pressure measured in pascals (Pa), V is the volume measured in m³, n is the number of moles, R is the gas constant (8.31 J K⁻¹ mol⁻¹) and T is the temperature in kelvin.

Exam tip

It is essential that the quantities in this equation have the correct units — notice in particular that volume of gas is in m³, not cm³ or dm³.

In an experiment, 0.700 mol of CO_2 was produced. This gas occupied a volume of $0.0450\,m^3$ at a pressure of 100 kPa. Calculate the temperature of the CO_2 and state the units of your answer.

Answer

$pV = nRT$

$p = 100\,000\,Pa$ $V = 0.0450\,m^3$ $n = 0.700\,mol$ $R = 8.31\,J\,K^{-1}\,mol^{-1}$

Substituting gives:

$100\,000 \times 0.0450 = 0.700 \times 8.31 \times T$

Rearranging gives:

$$T = \frac{100\,000 \times 0.0450}{0.700 \times 8.31} = 774\,K \text{ (to 3 significant figures)}$$

This temperature, in Celsius, would be $774 - 273 = 501°C$.

Now test yourself

TESTED

5 A 0.905 mol sample of hydrogen gas, H_2, occupies a volume of $0.0330\,m^3$ at a temperature of 200°C. What is the pressure exerted by the gas? The gas constant, R is $8.31\,J\,K^{-1}\,mol^{-1}$.

Answers on p. 100

The mole and reactions

Questions on the mole are asked on many examination papers, so it is essential that this type of question is mastered.

Mass calculations

REVISED

23.0 g of calcium carbonate decomposes fully on heating. Calculate the mass of carbon dioxide gas that forms. [A_r data: C = 12.0; Ca = 40.1; O = 16.0]

Answer

The equation for the reaction taking place is:

$CaCO_3(s) \rightarrow CaO(s) + CO_2(g)$

Step 1

Calculate the number of moles of calcium carbonate.

molar mass of $CaCO_3 = 40.1 + 12.0 + (3 \times 16.0) = 100.1\,g$

$$\text{number of mol of } CaCO_3 = \frac{\text{mass used (g)}}{\text{mass of 1 mol (g)}}$$

$$= \frac{23.0}{100.1} = 0.230\,mol$$

Step 2

From the equation, $CaCO_3(s) \rightarrow CaO(s) + CO_2(g)$, 1 mol of $CaCO_3$ gives 1 mol of CO_2; the ratio is 1 : 1. So, the amount of CO_2 that forms is also 0.230 mol.

Step 3

Calculate the mass of carbon dioxide.

mass of CO_2 = mass of 1 mol of CO_2 × number of mol

$= (12 + 16 + 16) \times 0.230 = 10.1\,g$ of CO_2 gas

Now test yourself

TESTED

6 Use the equation $Mg(s) + 2HCl(aq) \rightarrow MgCl_2(aq) + H_2(g)$ to determine the volume of hydrogen at 25°C that forms when 2.00 g of magnesium is added to excess hydrochloric acid.
[A_r data: Mg = 24.3; H = 1.0]

Answer on p. 100

Exam tip

Remember the three steps: **moles** (work out the moles); **ratio** (using the balanced symbol equation); calculate the **mass** of product (using moles × mass of 1 mol).

Gas calculations

REVISED

Equal volumes of gases contain equal numbers of particles, hence the amounts (in moles) will be the same.

Example

100 cm³ of hydrogen is reacted with (a) chlorine and (b) oxygen in reactions that go to completion (no reactants are left). What volume of gas is formed in each reaction?

Answer

(a) $H_2(g) + Cl_2(g) \rightarrow 2HCl(g)$
From the equation, 1 volume of H_2 reacts with 1 volume of Cl_2 to form 2 volumes of HCl.
So, 100 cm³ of H_2 reacts with 100 cm³ of Cl_2 to form 200 cm³ of HCl.
(b) $2H_2(g) + O_2(g) \rightarrow 2H_2O(g)$
2 volumes of hydrogen react with 1 volume of oxygen to form 2 volumes of water vapour.
So, 100 cm³ of hydrogen reacts with 50 cm³ of oxygen to form 100 cm³ of water vapour.

Revision activity

Using the internet, find out about the famous French chemist and physicist Joseph Louis Gay-Lussac.

Now test yourself

TESTED

7 What volume of hydrogen will react with 150 cm³ of nitrogen in the following reaction, assuming the reaction goes to completion?

$N_2(g) + 3H_2(g) \rightarrow 2NH_3(g)$

Answer on p. 100

Other reactions involving gases

Example

Calculate the volume of gas produced at 298 K and 100 kPa when 1.45 g of lithium metal reacts with water. [A_r data: Li = 6.9]

Answer

$2Li(s) + 2H_2O(l) \rightarrow 2LiOH(aq) + H_2(g)$

amount of lithium $= \dfrac{1.45}{6.9} = 0.210$ mol

amount of hydrogen produced will be $\dfrac{0.210}{2}$ (according to the ratios in the equation)

So:

amount of hydrogen = 0.105 mol

volume of hydrogen $= \dfrac{nRT}{p} = \dfrac{0.105 \times 8.31 \times 298}{100\,000}$

$= 2.600 \times 10^{-3}\,m^3$ or 2600 cm^3

Revision activity

On a revision card, write formulae for how the amount of substance can be worked out for solids, solutions and gases. You will find these formulae very useful.

Now test yourself

8 What volume of oxygen forms at room temperature and pressure when 100 cm^3 of a 0.500 mol dm^{-3} solution of hydrogen peroxide decomposes according to this equation?

$2H_2O_2(aq) \rightarrow 2H_2O(l) + O_2(g)$

Answer on p. 100

Solutions

The basic relationship for the amount of a substance in a solution can be expressed as:

amount of solute dissolved (mol) $= \dfrac{\text{volume of solution (cm}^3) \times \text{concentration (mol dm}^{-3})}{1000\,\text{cm}^3}$

It is also possible to convert everything into dm^3 and use:

amount of solute dissolved (mol) = volume of solution (dm^3) × concentration (mol dm^{-3})

Example

Calculate the number of moles of acid dissolved in 25.50 cm^3 of 2.50 × 10^{-3} mol dm^{-3} sulfuric acid.

Answer

number of mol $= \dfrac{25.50\,\text{cm}^3}{1000\,\text{cm}^3} \times 2.5 \times 10^{-3}\,\text{mol dm}^{-3}$

$= 6.375 \times 10^{-5}$ mol of H_2SO_4

Now test yourself

9 How many moles of solute are dissolved in:
   (a) $10.0\,cm^3$ of $0.200\,mol\,dm^{-3}$ NaOH?
   (b) $250\,cm^3$ of $1.20\,mol\,dm^{-3}$ HNO_3?

Answer on p. 101

Solutions and reactions

Many reactions are carried out in solution. Calculations involving reacting amounts and volumes of solutions are common in examinations.

Example

Calculate the volume of $0.200\,mol\,dm^{-3}$ sulfuric acid required to react exactly with $10.5\,cm^3$ of $0.400\,mol\,dm^{-3}$ sodium hydroxide solution.

Answer

$$2NaOH(aq) + H_2SO_4(aq) \rightarrow Na_2SO_4(aq) + 2H_2O(l)$$

$$\text{number of moles of sodium hydroxide} = \frac{10.5}{1000} \times 0.400 = 4.2 \times 10^{-3}\,mol$$

According to the equation, $4.2 \times 10^{-3}\,mol$ of sodium hydroxide reacts with $\frac{1}{2}(4.2 \times 10^{-3})$ moles of sulfuric acid (the reacting ratio according to the equation is $2:1$). So, 2.1×10^{-3} moles of sulfuric acid are required. If the starting concentration is $0.2\,mol\,dm^{-3}$, then:

$$2.10 \times 10^{-3}\,mol = \frac{\text{volume in } cm^3}{1000\,cm^3} \times 0.200\,mol\,dm^{-3}$$

Rearranging, the volume is calculated as:

$$\frac{2.10 \times 10^{-3} \times 1000}{0.200} = 10.5\,cm^3$$

> **Exam tip**
>
> The stages involved in this type of calculation are the same as with mass calculations — work out the moles followed by the reaction ratio, and finally the volume (or concentration).

> **Revision activity**
>
> Write out the key stages involved in carrying out an acid–base titration. Find out why this method of working is considered to be very accurate.

Now test yourself

10 Calculate the volume of $0.0500\,mol\,dm^{-3}$ NaOH that will react exactly with $20.0\,cm^3$ of $0.900\,mol\,dm^{-3}$ HCl.

Answer on p. 101

Percentage atom economy

Sustainable development involves maximising our use of the resources available and reducing waste products if at all possible.

In a reaction, a measure of how much of the total mass of reactants is converted into the desired product is called the **atom economy** of that reaction, and is defined as:

$$\frac{\text{maximum mass of product}}{\text{total mass of all products}} \times 100$$

Or as:

$$\frac{\text{mass of product}}{\text{total } M_r \text{ values for all reactants}} \times 100$$

> **Exam tip**
>
> The symbols A_r and M_r mean *relative* atomic mass and *relative* molecular mass respectively. Neither term has any units as they are relative, or comparative.

Example

Calculate the atom economy for ethanol formation in this process:

$$C_6H_{12}O_6(aq) \rightarrow 2C_2H_5OH(aq) + 2CO_2(g)$$

Answer

M_r of glucose = 180, so the percentage atom economy will be:

$$\frac{2 \times 46}{180} \times 100 = 51.1\%$$

Now test yourself

11 What is the atom economy for the formation of chloromethane in the reaction:

$$CH_4(g) + Cl_2(g) \rightarrow CH_3Cl(g) + HCl(g)$$

M_r for CH_3Cl is 50.5 and for HCl it is 36.5.

Answer on p. 101

Percentage yield

In a reaction, the amount of product is called its **yield**:

$$\% \text{ yield} = \frac{\text{mass of product formed}}{\text{maximum theoretical mass of product}} \times 100$$

Example

When a 15.0 g sample of magnesium is heated in oxygen, it is found that 22.2 g of magnesium oxide forms. What is the percentage yield? [A_r data: Mg = 24.3; O = 16.0]

Answer

Write the chemical equation for the reaction:

$$2Mg(s) + O_2(g) \rightarrow 2MgO(s)$$

Calculate the actual mass of magnesium oxide expected:

amount of magnesium = $\frac{15.0}{24.3}$ = 0.617 mol

amount of MgO formed = 0.617 mol

mass of MgO = 0.617 × 40.3 = 24.9 g

The yield is therefore $\frac{22.2}{24.9}$ × 100 = 89.2% (to 3 significant figures).

Chemical formulae and writing chemical equations

Formulae of common ions

REVISED

The ability to write correct formulae is an important skill and should be practised. The same is true of chemical equations. Table 2.1 lists some formulae of common ions that are worth knowing.

Table 2.1 Some common ions

Formula of ion	Name of ion
CO_3^{2-}	Carbonate
SO_4^{2-}	Sulfate(vi)
NO_3^-	Nitrate(v)
NH_4^+	Ammonium
OH^-	Hydroxide
SO_3^{2-}	Sulfate(iv) or sulfite
NO_2^-	Nitrate(iii) or nitrite
HCO_3^-	Hydrogencarbonate
SiO_3^{2-}	Silicate
ClO_3^-	Chlorate(v)
PO_4^{3-}	Phosphate(v)

> **Revision activity**
>
> On a revision card, write down the ions in this table and try to remember them. Keep looking at the card until you know them all. Alternatively, you could write the formulae of the ions into a simple database and use it to test yourself.

You can work out the formulae for some common compounds using a periodic table for reference.

> **Example**
>
> What is the formula for each of these compounds:
> (a) magnesium oxide
> (b) copper(i) sulfide
> (c) manganese(ii) nitrate
> (d) ammonium sulfate?
>
> *Answer*
>
> (a) Magnesium oxide is made up of Mg^{2+} and O^{2-} ions. The charges will cancel so the formula is MgO.
> (b) Copper(i) sulfide is made of Cu^+ and S^{2-} ions, swapping over the charges (or valencies) gives Cu_2S.
> (c) Manganese(ii) nitrate is made of Mn^{2+} and NO_3^- ions. Swapping over the numbers gives $Mn(NO_3)_2$. Remember to use a bracket when multiplying more than one element by a number.
> (d) Ammonium sulfate is made of ammonium ions, NH_4^+, and sulfate ions, SO_4^{2-}. Swapping over the valencies gives $(NH_4)_2SO_4$.

> **Exam tip**
>
> When deducing the formula for a compound made of ions, simply swap over the charges, or valencies, in their lowest ratio.

Now test yourself

TESTED

12 What is the formula for each of these compounds?
  (a) sodium fluoride
  (b) potassium sulfate
  (c) aluminium hydroxide?

Answers on p. 101

Table 2.2 lists some important substances have formulae that are easier to know, rather than work out.

Table 2.2

Substance	Formulae
Sulfuric acid	H_2SO_4
Nitric acid	HNO_3
Hydrochloric acid	HCl
Hydrogen peroxide	H_2O_2
Ammonia	NH_3
Alkanes	C_nH_{2n+2}

Writing balanced symbol equations

Many reactants and products will be evident from the text of the examination question; others you will be expected to know. For example, the reactions of acids are very important — these are summarised in Figure 2.2.

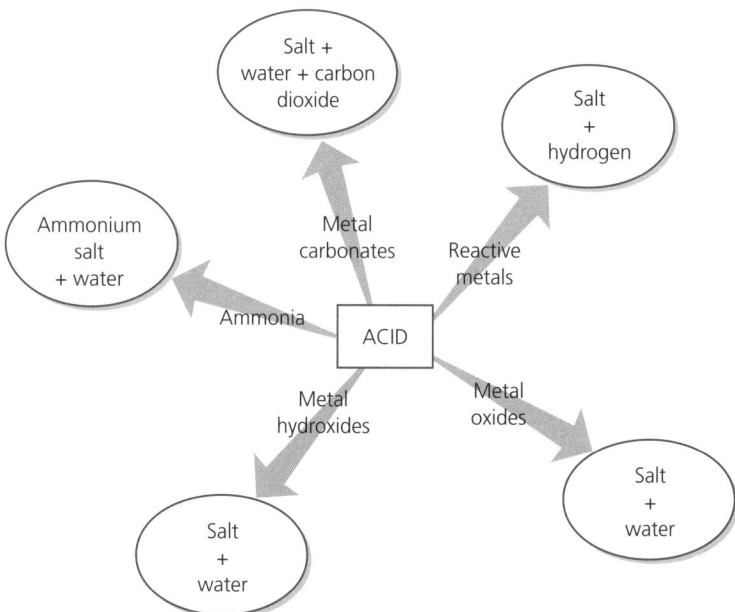

Figure 2.2 Reactions of acids

Example

Write a balanced equation to show how magnesium reacts with dilute nitric acid.

Answer

You need to know that magnesium nitrate and hydrogen gas form. You can then construct an equation and balance it.

● Write the formulae for each of the reactants and products:

$$Mg + HNO_3 \rightarrow Mg(NO_3)_2 + H_2$$

● Balance to make it into an equation:

$$Mg + 2HNO_3 \rightarrow Mg(NO_3)_2 + H_2$$

● Add state symbols if they are known:

$$Mg(s) + 2HNO_3(aq) \rightarrow Mg(NO_3)_2(aq) + H_2(g)$$

TESTED

13 Write a balanced symbol equation for the displacement reaction that takes place between aluminium metal and copper(II) sulfate.

Answers on p. 101

Ionic equations

REVISED

Ionic equations are useful for some reactions because they do not include spectator ions — just those ions that do take part in the reaction.

Consider the reaction mentioned previously:

$$Mg(s) + 2HNO_3(aq) \rightarrow Mg(NO_3)_2(aq) + H_2(g)$$

To convert this into an ionic equation, any substance that is dissolved in water has to be written out in its ionic form:

$$Mg(s) + 2H^+(aq) + 2NO_3^-(aq) \rightarrow Mg^{2+}(aq) + 2NO_3^-(aq) + H_2(g)$$

You then cancel out the spectator ions, in this case the nitrate ions, NO_3^-. This leaves:

$$Mg(s) + 2H^+(aq) \rightarrow Mg^{2+}(aq) + H_2(g)$$

which is the ionic equation for the reaction.

> **Exam tip**
>
> It is sometimes easier to remember the common types of ionic equation — neutralisation is $H^+(aq) + OH^-(aq) \rightarrow H_2O(l)$.

TESTED

14 Write a balanced equation and an ionic equation to show potassium hydroxide solution reacting with hydrochloric acid. Include state symbols in your answer.

Answers on p. 101

Exam practice

1 Fluorine is a pale yellow gas that is known to be extremely reactive. It reacts with magnesium according to the equation:

$$Mg(s) + F_2(g) \rightarrow MgF_2(s)$$

In an experiment, 9.20 g of magnesium react with excess fluorine and magnesium fluoride is formed. [A_r data: Mg = 24.3; F = 19.0]
(a) Calculate the number of moles of magnesium used in the experiment. [1]
(b) Calculate the number of moles of magnesium fluoride formed in the reaction. [1]
(c) What mass of magnesium fluoride is formed? [1]
(d) What mass of magnesium would be needed if exactly 50.0 g of magnesium fluoride is required? [3]

2 In a titration, 25.00 cm³ of 0.500 mol dm⁻³ sodium hydroxide is poured into to a conical flask and then titrated with hydrochloric acid of unknown concentration. It is found that 14.50 cm³ of the acid is required for complete neutralisation. The equation for the reaction is:

$$HCl(aq) + NaOH(aq) \rightarrow NaCl(aq) + H_2O(l)$$

(a) Calculate the number of moles of sodium hydroxide used. [1]
(b) Deduce the number of moles of acid added from the burette. [1]
(c) Calculate the concentration of the dilute hydrochloric acid in mol dm⁻³. [1]

3 The element indium forms a compound X with hydrogen and oxygen. Compound X contains 69.2% indium and 1.8% hydrogen by mass. Calculate the empirical formula of X. [A_r data: In = 114.8; H = 1.0; O = 16.0] [3]

4 An unknown metal carbonate reacts with hydrochloric acid according to the equation:

$$M_2CO_3(aq) + 2HCl(aq) \rightarrow 2MCl(aq) + CO_2(g) + H_2O(l)$$

A 1.72 g sample of M_2CO_3 was dissolved in distilled water to make 250 cm³ of solution. A 25.0 cm³ portion of this solution required 16.6 cm³ of 0.150 mol dm⁻³ hydrochloric acid for complete reaction.

(a) Calculate the amount of HCl used. Give your answer to 3 significant figures. [1]
(b) Deduce the amount of M_2CO_3 that reacted with the hydrochloric acid. [1]
(c) How many moles of M_2CO_3 must have been present in the 250 cm³ of solution? [1]
(d) What is the relative formula mass, M_r, of M_2CO_3? [1]
(e) Deduce the relative atomic mass of metal M. [1]

5 This question is about reactions of calcium compounds.
A pure solid is thought to be calcium hydroxide. The solid can be identified from its relative formula mass. The relative formula mass can be determined experimentally by reacting a measured mass of the pure solid with an excess of hydrochloric acid.
The equation for this reaction is $Ca(OH)_2 + 2HCl \rightarrow CaCl_2 + 2H_2O$.
The unreacted acid can then be determined by titration with a standard sodium hydroxide solution. You are provided with 50.0 cm³ of 0.200 mol dm⁻³ hydrochloric acid.
Outline, giving brief practical details, how you would conduct an accurate experiment to calculate the relative formula mass of the solid using this method. [8]

6 Which of these pieces of apparatus has the lowest percentage error in the measurement shown? [1]
  A Volume of 25 cm³ measured with a burette with an error of ±0.1 cm³.
  B Volume of 25 cm³ measured with a measuring cylinder with an error of ±0.5 cm³.
  C Mass of 0.150 g measured with a balance with an error of ±0.001 g.
  D Temperature change of 23.2°C measured with a thermometer with an error of ±0.1°C.

7 A student is provided with a 5.00 cm³ sample of 1.00×10^{-2} mol dm⁻³ hydrochloric acid.
The student is asked to devise a method to prepare a hydrochloric acid solution with a concentration of 5.00×10^{-4} mol dm⁻³ by diluting the sample with water.
Which of these is the correct volume of water that should be added? [1]
  A 45.0 cm³
  B 95.0 cm³
  C 100 cm³
  D 995 cm³

Answers and quick quiz 2 online ONLINE

Summary

You should now have an understanding of:
- what is meant by the term 'mole'
- the Avogadro constant
- empirical formulae and molecular formulae
- the ideal gas equation
- how to carry out solid, gas and solution calculations
- percentage atom economy and its implications
- percentage yield
- how to write chemical equations and ionic equations

3 Bonding

Nature of ionic, covalent and metallic bonds

All types of chemical bond — whether ionic, covalent or metallic — are due to electrostatic attractions between positively charged and negatively charged particles.

Ionic bonding

Dot-and-cross diagrams (Figure 3.1) show how atoms form ions when electrons are **transferred** from a metal atom (which becomes a positively charged ion) to a non-metal atom (which becomes a negatively charged ion).

> **Ionic bonding** happens between oppositely charged **ions** in a lattice.

Figure 3.1 Dot-and-cross diagram for the formation of Ca^{2+} and Cl^-

Oppositely charged ions are attracted to each other by strong electrostatic forces. This makes it difficult to separate the ions from each other. Therefore, ionic substances:
- have high melting points
- are good electrical conductors when molten and in solution (when the ions are free to move) but poor electrical conductors when solid (when the ions are fixed in their lattice and are not free to move)

When ions pack together, they form a giant ionic structure in which positive and negatively charged ions are arranged in a lattice (Figure 3.2).

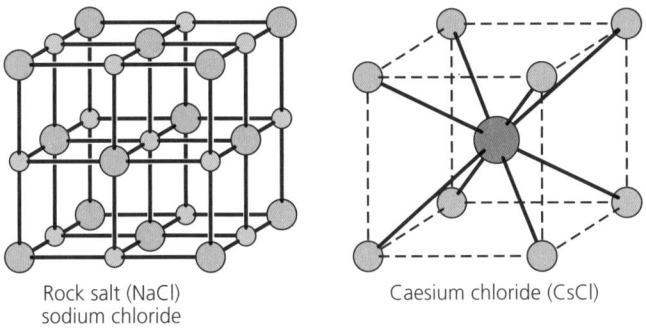

Rock salt (NaCl)
sodium chloride

Caesium chloride (CsCl)

Figure 3.2 Diagrams showing part-structures for NaCl and CsCl

Now test yourself

TESTED

1 Draw dot-and-cross diagrams to show the bonding in (a) magnesium oxide and (b) sodium oxide. [Atomic number data: Mg = 12; O = 8; Na = 11]
2 Explain why lithium fluoride has a high melting point.

Answers on p. 101

Covalent bonding

REVISED

Atoms may covalently bond together to form **molecules**. These molecules may be very easy to separate because they are attracted to each other by weak intermolecular forces — these give the substance very low melting and boiling points. These substances have **simple covalent** structures (Figure 3.3).

> A **covalent bond** involves electron pairs being *shared* between atoms.

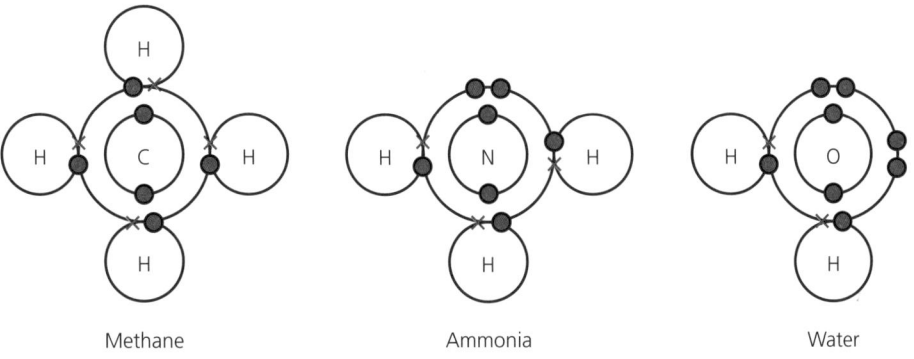

Methane

Ammonia

Water

Figure 3.3 Examples of simple covalent structures

Giant molecules, like diamond (Figure 3.4), can form in which atoms are bonded throughout the structure using strong covalent bonds. This gives substances a very high melting point because these bonds will require a lot of energy to break. These are called **giant covalent (or macromolecular) structures**.

Figure 3.4 Structure of diamond

Now test yourself   TESTED ☐

3 Draw dot-and-cross diagrams to show the bonding in (a) methane and (b) nitrogen.
   [Atomic number data: C = 6; H = 1; N = 7]
4 Explain why methane has a low melting point.

Answers on p. 101

Revision activity

Use the internet to look up other small molecules and see if you can draw their electronic structures, showing their covalent bonds.

Dative covalent (coordinate) bonding   REVISED ☐

In the formation of the ammonium ion, NH_4^+, the lone pair of electrons on the nitrogen atom is used to form a single covalent bond with a proton (Figure 3.5).

A dative covalent or **coordinate bond** is one in which both electrons being shared in the covalent bond come from the same atom.

Ammonia   Hydrogen ion   Ammonium ion

Figure 3.5 Formation of an ammonium ion, NH_4^+

Carbon monoxide and ozone, O_3, are examples of molecules that contain a dative bond in which two electrons are donated from the oxygen atom.

Now test yourself   TESTED ☐

5 Draw a dot-and-cross diagram for a carbon monoxide molecule.
   [Atomic number data: C = 6; O = 8]

Answer on p. 101

Metallic bonding

REVISED

Metals consist of a lattice of **positive ions** surrounded by **delocalised electrons** (Figure 3.6).

The mutual attraction of the positive ions for the delocalised electrons is a strong electrostatic force and gives most metals **high melting points** because it is difficult to separate the ions from each other.

The mobile electrons can carry an electrical charge and this explains why metals can conduct electricity so well.

The layers of metal ions within the lattice can also slide across each other fairly easily when a force is applied; this means that metals can be beaten into sheets and are said to **malleable**.

Delocalised electrons

Figure 3.6 Structure of a metal

> **Typical mistake**
>
> What is wrong with this student's answer in explaining why the electrical conductivity of a metal is good? 'Because there are mobile ions that can carry the charge.'
>
> They should have said that mobile *electrons* are free to carry the charge.

Bond polarity

Electronegativity

REVISED

Figure 3.7 shows the graph of electronegativity plotted against atomic number for the first 20 elements.

> **Electronegativity** is the power of an atom to withdraw electron density from a covalent bond.

Figure 3.7 How electronegativity varies with atomic number

Electronegativity increases across a period, from left to right, and decreases going down a group. Elements with very high electronegativity values include F, N and O — these elements are very good at attracting bonded electrons towards their nuclei. This attraction causes an **asymmetrical electron distribution** in which the electronegative atom develops a slight negative charge and the other atom develops a slight positive charge. A **polar bond** is produced.

Figure 3.8 shows the electron distribution in a chlorine molecule (a non-polar molecule because both atoms are the same) and hydrogen chloride (a polar molecule due to the different electronegativities of hydrogen (2.1) and chlorine (3.0)). Hydrogen chloride is a polar molecule and has slightly charged ends: $H^{\delta+}-Cl^{\delta-}$.

Chlorine molecule: symmetrical
electron distribution

Hydrogen chloride molecule:
asymmetrical electron distribution

Figure 3.8 Electron distribution in chlorine and hydrogen chloride

Exam tip

Elements have different
electronegativity values —
this means that bonds
can differ in their polarity
depending on the atoms at
the ends of the bond.

Now test yourself

TESTED

6 Explain why hydrogen fluoride, HF, is a polar molecule whereas
  hydrogen, H_2, is a non-polar molecule.
  The electronegativity values of fluorine and hydrogen are 4.0 and 2.1
  respectively.

Answer on p. 101

Some molecules may have polar bonds but the molecule still has no
overall **dipole moment**. This is because the individual dipoles cancel out
because of the three-dimensional shape of the molecule. An example of
this is carbon dioxide (Figure 3.9) in which the carbon–oxygen dipoles
cancel due to there being equal and opposite dipoles.

$$\overset{\delta-}{O}=\overset{\delta+}{C}=\overset{\delta-}{O}$$

**Figure 3.9
Carbon dioxide
molecule**

Forces acting between molecules

Forces acting between molecules are called **intermolecular forces**.
There are three main types and their strength decreases in the order:

hydrogen bonding > dipole–dipole forces > van der Waals forces

Molecules with permanent dipoles

REVISED

When a molecule has a permanent dipole, either dipole–dipole attractions
or hydrogen bonding are possible intermolecular forces.

Hydrogen bonding

If nitrogen, oxygen or fluorine atoms are covalently bonded to
hydrogen atoms in a molecule, for example in ammonia and water,
an intermolecular attraction called a **hydrogen bond** can act
between molecules.

A lone pair of electrons on an oxygen atom of one water molecule
is attracted to the slight positive charge on a hydrogen atom in a
neighbouring water molecule (Figure 3.10).

Exam tip

Forces that exist *within*
a molecule are strong
covalent bonds. Those
between molecules are weak
intermolecular forces.

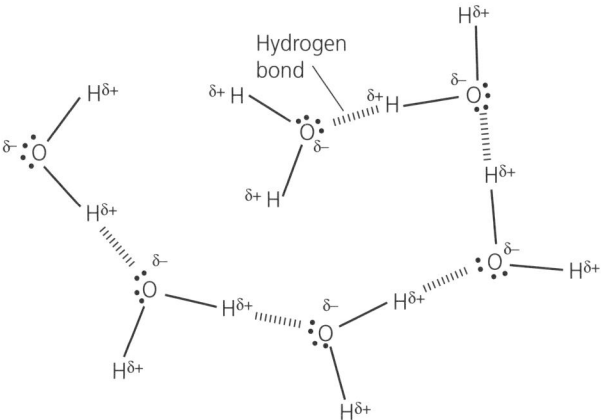

Figure 3.10 Hydrogen bonding in water

Water is a substance that has some anomalous physical properties that can be explained using hydrogen bonding:
- higher melting and boiling points than expected
- lower density as a ice than as a liquid
- the existence of surface tension

Now test yourself

TESTED

7 Draw a diagram to show the hydrogen bonding that takes place between two molecules of ammonia. Make sure that you include all lone pairs and partial charges in your diagram.

Answer on p. 101

Dipole–dipole attractions

Polar molecules that do not have N, O or F atoms bonded directly to hydrogen atoms can attract each other using **dipole–dipole attractions**. This is a weaker intermolecular force than hydrogen bonding.

Molecules of hydrogen chloride (Figure 3.11) can attract each other in this way — the slight negative charge on the chlorine atoms attracts the slight positive charge of hydrogen atoms on another molecule.

$$\overset{\delta+}{H} \text{——} \overset{\delta-}{Cl} \text{ - - - - - } \overset{\delta+}{H} \text{——} \overset{\delta-}{Cl}$$

Figure 3.11 Why molecules of hydrogen chloride interact

Molecules with temporary dipoles

REVISED

Many molecules are non-polar and yet they are still able to attract each other using **van der Waals forces**, the weakest of all intermolecular forces.

The electrons in all molecules are in constant motion and this movement causes 'wobbles' in electron clouds that result in temporary dipoles. This dipole may then induce another temporary dipole in a neighbouring molecule. The attraction between these temporary dipoles is called a van der Waals force.

The size of van der Waals forces depends on the number of electrons in a molecule and also the area of contact of one molecule with another.

Exam tip

The melting and boiling points of a homologous series of hydrocarbons and the elements in group 7 (the halogens) and group 0 (the noble gases) all increase as relative molecular mass increases. This is due to the increasing number of electrons in molecules.

Explain why the boiling points of the hydrocarbons — methane, ethane, propane, butane and pentane — increase in the order written.

Answer

As the relative molecular mass increases, the number of electrons in each molecule increases. This means that more and stronger van der Waals forces exist between the molecules, and they will be more difficult to separate from each other, giving them higher boiling points.

Now test yourself

TESTED

8 Explain why the boiling points of the halogens increase on descending the group.

Answers on p. 101

States of matter

Structure of substances

REVISED

Substances have different physical properties that depend on their structures (Figure 3.12).

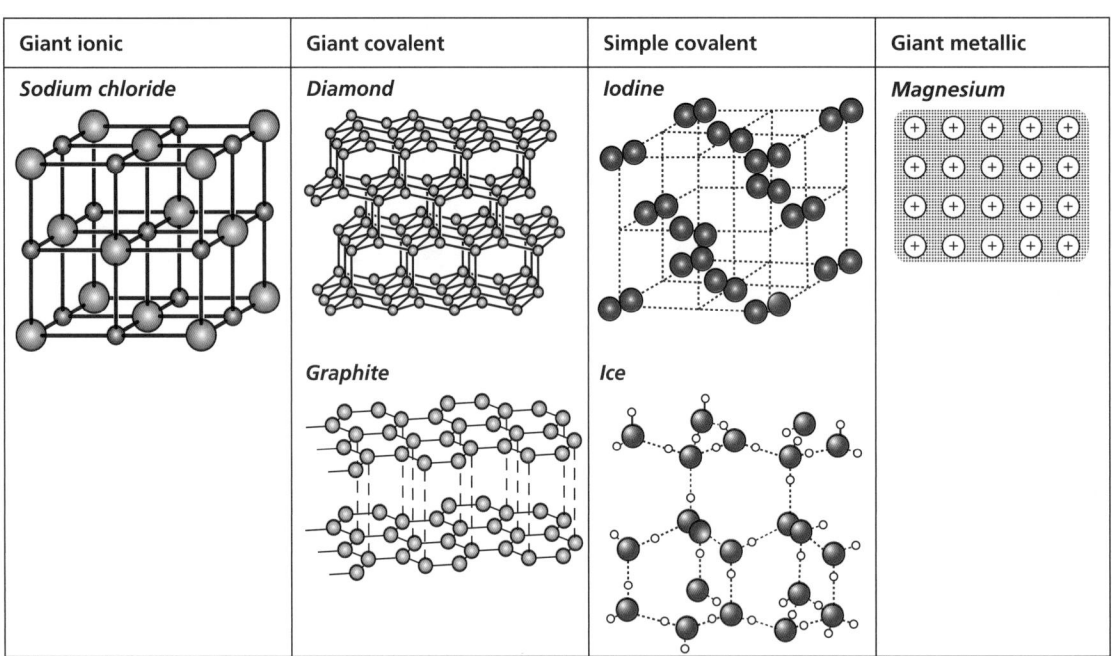

Giant ionic	Giant covalent	Simple covalent	Giant metallic
Sodium chloride	*Diamond*	*Iodine*	*Magnesium*
	Graphite	*Ice*	

Figure 3.12 Examples of substances with different structures

Giant ionic substances have high melting and boiling points because the oppositely charged ions are attracted to each other by strong electrostatic forces. They are good electrical conductors when molten and in solution because the ions are free to carry the electrical charge. In the solid state, the ions are fixed in place in the lattice.

Giant covalent (macromolecular) substances have high melting and boiling points because the atoms are bonded throughout by strong covalent bonds. This means that a lot of energy is required to break the bonds and to melt the substance.

Exam practice answers and quick quizzes at **www.hoddereducation.co.uk/myrevisionnotes**

Simple covalent substances have low melting and boiling points because it is relatively easy to overcome the weak intermolecular forces to separate one molecule from others.

Metallic substances generally have high melting and boiling points because there are strong electrostatic forces acting between the mobile electrons and the positive ions in the lattice. They are good electrical conductors because the electrons are free to move and carry the charge.

Now test yourself

TESTED

9 Explain why sodium fluoride, NaF, has a high melting point whereas the element fluorine, F_2, has a low melting point.

Answer on p. 101

Shapes of molecules and ions

Deducing the shape of a molecule

REVISED

The three-dimensional shape of a molecule depends on the repulsion of the electron pairs around the central atom in the molecule. The decreasing order of strengths of these is as follows:

lone pair–lone pair > lone pair–bonding pair > bonding pair–bonding pair

Table 3.1 The shapes of molecules

Number of bonding pairs around the central atom (or atom–atom links)	Number of non-bonding pairs	Name of shape with diagram and examples
2	0	Linear 180° ○—◉—○ CO_2, HCN, $BeCl_2$, $[Ag(NH_3)_2]^+$
2	2	Bent H_2O, H_2S, NO_2^-, ClO_2
3	0	Trigonal planar 120° BF_3, NO_3^-, CO_3^{2-}, SO_3
3	1	Pyramidal 107° NH_3, PH_3, SO_3^{2-}, ClO_3^-
3	2	T-shape ClF_3

Number of bonding pairs around the central atom (or atom–atom links)	Number of non-bonding pairs	Name of shape with diagram and examples
4	0	Tetrahedral 109°28' NH_4^+, CH_4, SO_4^{2-}, $CuCl_4^{2-}$
4	2	Square planar XeF_4, ICl_4^-
5	0	Trigonal bipyramidal 120° PCl_5
6	0	Octahedral SF_6, $[M(H_2O)_6]^{2+}$ where M = a metal ion

When working out the shape of a molecule or ion, you must work out the number of bonding electrons pairs and lone pairs.

Example

Deduce the shape of a hydrogen sulfide, H_2S, molecule.

Answer

- Sulfur is in group 6 of the periodic table and so its atoms have six outer electrons.
- Each hydrogen atom shares one electron to make a single covalent bond.
- This means there are four pairs of outer electrons — two bonding pairs and two lone pairs.
- Lone pairs repel the bonding pairs slightly more strongly than the bonding pairs repel each other, so the internal angle is slightly less than the tetrahedral angle (109.5°).
- The shape name is bent (non-linear) and the internal angle is about 104.5° (Figure 3.13).

Figure 3.13 **A hydrogen sulfide molecule**

Exam tip

As a 'rule of thumb', each lone pair causes the expected tetrahedral angle to decrease by about 2.5°. So, two lone pairs of electrons would cause a decrease of about 5° from 109.5° — hence 104.5° (as in water and hydrogen sulfide).

Example

Deduce the shape of a PF_6^- ion.

Answer

- Phosphorus is in group 5 of the periodic table and so its atoms have five outer electrons.
- Each fluorine atom shares one electron to make a single covalent bond, contributing six electrons to the outer layer.
- The negative charge on the ion adds one more electron.
- The total number of electrons around the phosphorus atom is 5 + 6 + 1 = 12, meaning six bonding pairs. There are no lone pairs.
- The shape (Figure 3.14) will therefore be octahedral and the internal bond angles will be 90° and 180°.

Figure 3.14 **A phosphorus(v) hexafluoride ion**

Now test yourself

TESTED ☐

10 Sketch the shapes and indicate the internal bond angles and shape names of each of these covalent particles:
   (a) NH_4^+
   (b) BF_3
   (c) SF_6

Answer on p. 101

Exam practice

1 (a) Describe, with a diagram, the lattice structure of sodium chloride. [2]
   (b) Using your diagram from part (a), explain why sodium chloride has these properties:
      (i) Sodium chloride is a good electrical conductor when molten but not when solid.
      (ii) Sodium chloride has a high melting point. [2]
2 Explain the meaning of these terms:
   (a) covalent bond [2]
   (b) dative bond [2]
   (c) giant covalent (macromolecular) structure. [2]
3 (a) Draw a dot-and-cross diagram for boron trifluoride, BF_3. [2]
   (b) Comment on the outer electronic structure of the boron atom in boron trifluoride. [1]
   (c) Considering your previous answers, indicate how boron trifluoride may react with ammonia. [2]
4 (a) State the strongest type of intermolecular force present in water and the strongest type of intermolecular force in hydrogen sulfide (H_2S). [2]
   (b) Draw a diagram to show how two molecules of water are attracted to each other by the type of intermolecular force you stated in part (a). [3]
   (c) Explain why the boiling point of water is much higher than the boiling point of hydrogen sulfide. [2]
   (d) Explain why the boiling points increase from H_2S to H_2Te in group 6. [2]

5 Which of these species has a trigonal planar structure? [1]
   A PH_3
   B BCl_3
   C H_3O^+
   D CH_3^-

6 Use your understanding of intermolecular forces to predict which of these compounds
   has the highest boiling point. [1]
   A HF
   B HCl
   C HBr
   D HI

7 Which type of bond is formed between N and B when a molecule of NH_3 reacts with a
   molecule of BF_3? [1]
   A ionic
   B covalent
   C coordinate (dative)
   D van der Waals

Answers and quick quiz 3 online

ONLINE

Summary

You should now have an understanding of:
- ionic bonding
- covalent bonding
- dative (coordinate) bonding
- metallic bonding
- bond polarity and electronegativity

- hydrogen bonding
- dipole–dipole forces
- van der Waals forces
- the relationship between physical properties and structure
- shapes of molecules and ions

4 Energetics

Enthalpy change, ΔH

An enthalpy change, ΔH, is defined as the heat energy change at constant pressure. If the enthalpy change is a standard value, with the symbol $\Delta H^\ominus_{298}$, then particular conditions are specified: 100 kPa pressure and a temperature of 298 K.

The sign of ΔH

In a chemical process, heat energy can move either from the surroundings to the chemical system or vice versa. If heat energy moves from the system to the surroundings, the chemicals lose heat energy — an **exothermic reaction** results and the sign of ΔH is negative. If heat energy is transferred from the surroundings to the system, an **endothermic reaction** results and the sign of ΔH is positive.

Calorimetry

Calculations

Calorimetry is an experimental method for determining enthalpy changes. Simple reactions can be studied in this way. When calculating the enthalpy change for a reaction, it is usually necessary to convert from a temperature change measurement recorded in an experiment (in which water is heated or cooled) into a heat energy measurement, in J. This is done using the relationship:

$q = mc\Delta T$

- q is the quantity of heat energy, in J
- m is the mass of the water, in g
- c is the specific heat capacity of water, $4.18\,J\,K^{-1}\,g^{-1}$
- ΔT is the temperature change in °C or K

> **Typical mistake**
>
> Many students forget that m is the mass of water and not the mass of any solid used in the experiment.

Example 1

Calculate the enthalpy change (in $kJ\,mol^{-1}$), for the following reaction of magnesium ($A_r = 24.3$).

2.00 g of magnesium powder is added to an excess of $25.0\,cm^3$ of dilute sulfuric acid solution and the temperature is found to increase by 52.4°C.

Answer

Using $q = mc\Delta T$:

$m = 25.0\,g;\ c = 4.18\,J\,K^{-1}\,g^{-1};\ \Delta T = 52.4°C$

$q = 25.0 \times 4.18 \times 52.4 = 5476\,J = 5.476\,kJ$

$\text{amount of magnesium used} = \dfrac{2.00}{24.3} = 0.0823\,mol$

$\text{heat energy released} = \dfrac{q\ (\text{in kJ})}{\text{amount (in mol)}} = \dfrac{5.476}{0.0823} = 66.5\,kJ\,mol^{-1}$

The reaction is exothermic, so ΔH is negative, so the enthalpy change is $-66.5\,kJ\,mol^{-1}$.

Example 2

The following experiment was carried out in which a sample of ethanol (M_r = 46.0) was put into a spirit burner (Figure 4.1). The ethanol was ignited and the temperature of the 100 cm³ of water in the metal calorimeter was found to increase from 20.1°C to 52.6°C. The mass of the spirit burner decreased from 35.64 g to 35.14 g. Calculate the enthalpy of combustion of ethanol.

Figure 4.1 **Measuring an enthalpy of combustion**

Answer

Using $q = mc\Delta T$:

m = 100.0 g; c = 4.18 J K⁻¹ g⁻¹; ΔT = 52.6 − 20.1 = 32.5°C

q = 100 × 4.18 × 32.5 = 13 585 J = 13.59 kJ

amount of ethanol used = mass of ethanol combusted/M_r for ethanol

$= \dfrac{35.64 - 35.14}{46.0} = 0.0109$ mol

heat energy released $= \dfrac{q \text{ (in kJ)}}{\text{amount (in mol)}} = \dfrac{13.59}{0.0109} = 1247$ kJ mol⁻¹

The reaction is exothermic, so ΔH is negative, and the enthalpy change is −1250 kJ mol⁻¹.

Now test yourself

1 In an experiment, 0.95 g of powdered zinc (A_r = 65.4) is added to an excess of 25.0 cm³ of 2.00 mol dm⁻³ hydrochloric acid. The temperature rises by 11.4°C. Calculate the enthalpy change, in kJ mol⁻¹, for this reaction. The specific heat capacity of water is 4.18 J °C⁻¹ g⁻¹.

2 In an experiment, 0.16 g of methanol (CH_3OH, M_r = 32.0) is combusted when a spirit burner heats 100 cm³ of water from 17.0°C to 25.0°C. Calculate the enthalpy change of combustion of methanol.

Answers on p. 102

Simple applications of Hess's Law

Enthalpy of formation and combustion

REVISED

The **standard enthalpy of formation**, $\Delta_f H^\ominus$, is defined as the heat (or enthalpy) change when 1 mol of a compound is formed from its constituent elements, all reactants and products in their standard states at 298 K and 100 kPa pressure.

The standard enthalpy of formation, $\Delta_f H^\ominus$, for any *element* in its standard state is, by definition, taken as zero.

> **Hess's law** states that the enthalpy change of a process is independent of the route taken, whether it be direct or indirect.

Equations to represent the enthalpy of formation of sodium chloride and of ethane gas in which 1 mol of the compound is formed are as follows:

$$Na(s) + \tfrac{1}{2}Cl_2(g) \rightarrow NaCl(s)$$

$$2C(s) + 3H_2(g) \rightarrow C_2H_6(g)$$

The **standard enthalpy of combustion**, $\Delta_c H^\ominus$, is defined as the enthalpy change when 1 mol of a substance is completely burned in oxygen under standard conditions — 298 K and 100 kPa pressure — with all reactants and products in their standard states.

For example, the equation that represents the enthalpy of combustion of liquid methanol ($CH_3OH(l)$) is:

$$CH_3OH(l) + 1\tfrac{1}{2}O_2(g) \rightarrow CO_2(g) + 2H_2O(l)$$

Determining unknown enthalpies

REVISED

Cycle 1: using enthalpies of formation

Consider the following reaction, for which the enthalpy change is unknown:

$$4NH_3(g) + 5O_2(g) \rightarrow 4NO(g) + 6H_2O(l)$$

$\Delta_f H^\ominus$ values (in $kJ\,mol^{-1}$) are: NO(g) = +90.4; H_2O(l) = −286; NH_3(g) = −46.2.

Applying Hess's law, the enthalpy change, $\Delta H^\ominus$, for this reaction can be determined by drawing an energy cycle using the $\Delta_f H^\ominus$ values, as in Figure 4.2.

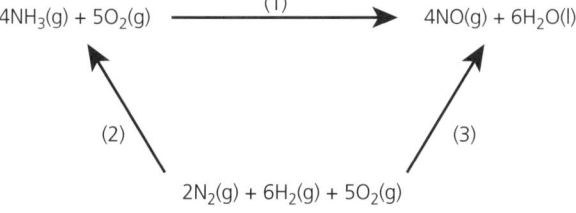

Figure 4.2

Using the cycle, it can be seen that enthalpy change (1) = −(2) + (3) = (3) − (2).

Letting $\Delta H^\ominus$ represent (1):

$$\Delta H^\ominus = 4\Delta_f H^\ominus[NO(g)] + 6\Delta_f H^\ominus[H_2O(l)] - 4\Delta_f H^\ominus[NH_3(g)] - 5\Delta_f H^\ominus[O_2(g)]$$

Substituting the appropriate given enthalpy of formation data gives:

$$\Delta H^{\ominus} = (4 \times 90.4) + (6 \times -286) - (4 \times -46.2) - (5 \times 0) = -1170\,\text{kJ}$$

Now test yourself

TESTED

3 Write balanced equations that represent the standard enthalpies of formation of these substances:
   (a) carbon dioxide, $CO_2(g)$
   (b) hexane, $C_6H_{14}(l)$
4 Calculate the enthalpy change for the reaction:

$$P_4O_{10}(s) + 6H_2O(l) \rightarrow 4H_3PO_4(l)$$

given the following standard enthalpies of formation (in $kJ\,mol^{-1}$):
$P_4O_{10}(s) = -2984.0$; $H_2O(l) = -285.8$; $H_3PO_4(l) = -1279$.

Answers on p. 102

Answers on p. 102

> **Exam tip**
>
> It is sometimes more convenient to remember that if a question asks for $\Delta H^{\ominus}$ to be determined and only $\Delta_f H^{\ominus}$ data are provided, then:
>
> $$\Delta H^{\ominus} = \Sigma\Delta_f H^{\ominus}(\text{products}) - \Sigma\Delta_f H^{\ominus}(\text{reactants})$$

Cycle 2: Using enthalpies of combustion

Example

Determine $\Delta_f H^{\ominus}$ for methane, given that the enthalpies of combustion of methane, carbon and hydrogen are −890.4, −393.5 and −285.8 $kJ\,mol^{-1}$ respectively.

Answer

The equation representing the enthalpy of formation of methane is:

$$C(s) + 2H_2(g) \rightarrow CH_4(g)$$

Figure 4.3 shows a cycle that has this equation across the top, and the combustions down the sides.

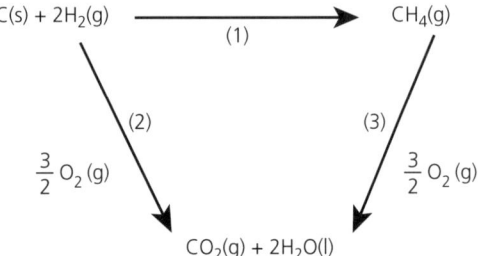

Figure 4.3

enthalpy change for the direct route from elements to oxides = (2)

enthalpy change for the indirect route from elements to oxides = (1) + (3)

Hence:

(2) = (1) + (3) or (1) = (2) − (3)

$$\Delta_f H^{\ominus}[CH_4(g)] = \Delta_c H^{\ominus}[C(s)] + 2\Delta_c H^{\ominus}[H_2(g)] - \Delta_c H^{\ominus}[CH_4(g)]$$

$$= -393.5 + (2 \times -285.8) - (-890.4) = -74.7\,kJ\,mol^{-1}$$

Now test yourself

5 Use the data below to calculate the enthalpy of formation of propane.

$C(s) + O_2(g) \rightarrow CO_2(g)$ $\Delta H = -393.5\,kJ\,mol^{-1}$

$H_2(g) + \frac{1}{2}O_2(g) \rightarrow H_2O(l)$ $\Delta H = -285.8\,kJ\,mol^{-1}$

$C_3H_8(g) + 5O_2(g) \rightarrow 3CO_2(g) + 4H_2O(l)$ $\Delta H = -2220.0\,kJ\,mol^{-1}$

Answer on p. 102

Bond enthalpies

Mean bond energy

A **mean bond energy** is defined as the average energy required to break 1 mol of specified bonds in the gas phase measured under standard conditions (298 K and 100 kPa pressure) over several different compounds containing the bond of interest.

- The average bond enthalpy of the N−H bond is +388 kJ mol⁻¹. This means that 388 kJ of heat energy are required to break 1 mol of N−H bonds in the gas phase. The decomposition of 1 mol of ammonia to form its constituent gaseous atoms:

$NH_3(g) \rightarrow N(g) + 3H(g)$

would require $3 \times 388\,kJ$ of heat energy, that is, 1164 kJ, because three N−H bonds are being broken.

- For a hydrogen molecule, the change $H-H(g) \rightarrow 2H(g)$ represents the bond energy of the H−H bond; this has a value of +436 kJ mol⁻¹. However, unlike the H−H bond, many other covalent bonds (for example C−H, C−C, C=O and N−H) vary in their strength depending on the molecule in which the bond is present. For this reason, *mean* bond energies are quoted for covalent bonds.

- Bond energies are always endothermic because energy must be provided to overcome the electrostatic attraction between the shared electrons in the covalent bond and the positively charged nuclei.

> **Exam tip**
>
> Experimental enthalpy values may differ from calculated mean bond energies. This is because mean bond energies are averages and not compound-specific values.

Example

Calculate $\Delta H^\ominus$ for the following reaction using mean bond energies:

$$CH_4(g) + 2Br_2(g) \rightarrow CH_2Br_2(g) + 2HBr(g)$$

Answer

The mean bond energies, in kJ mol⁻¹, are: C–H = +412; Br–Br = +193; C–Br = +276; H–Br = +366.

The energy cycle shown in Figure 4.4 can be drawn to represent the reaction.

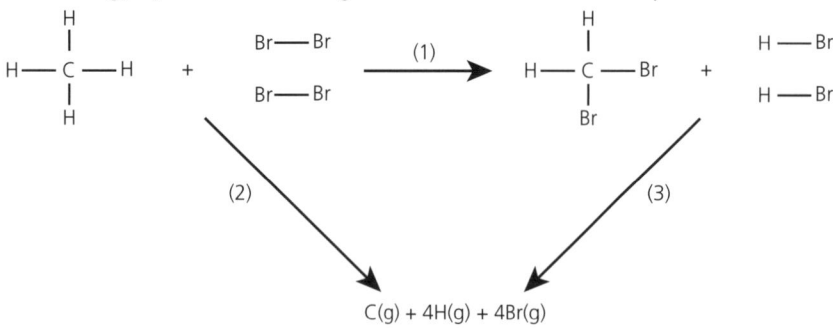

Figure 4.4

From the cycle, it can be seen that (1) = (2) – (3).

Using E to represent mean bond energy:

$\Delta H(1) = (4 \times E[\text{C–H}]) + (2 \times E[\text{Br–Br}]) - (2 \times E[\text{C–H}]) - (2 \times E[\text{C–Br}]) - (2 \times E[\text{H–Br}])$

Substituting the relevant bond energies gives:

$(4 \times 412) + (2 \times 193) - (2 \times 412) - (2 \times 276) - (2 \times 366) = -74\,\text{kJ mol}^{-1}$

Exam tip

In bond energy calculations, it is sometimes easier to remember:

ΔH = bond-breaking energy – bond-making energy

Or simply 'break minus make'.

Now test yourself

TESTED

6 The mean bond energies N=N = 409, H–H = 436, N–H = 388 and N–N = 163 are in kJ mol⁻¹.
   Calculate the approximate enthalpy change, ΔH, for this reaction of hydrogen:

$$N_2H_2(g) + H_2(g) \rightarrow N_2H_4(g)$$

Answer on p. 102

Exam practice answers and quick quizzes at **www.hoddereducation.co.uk/myrevisionnotes**

4 Energetics

Exam practice

1 The aim of this question is to determine the enthalpy change for the reaction between 0.56 g of calcium (A_r = 40.1) and 25.0 cm^3 of 2.0 mol dm^{-3} dilute hydrochloric acid. The initial temperature of the hydrochloric acid is 21.1°C and it reaches a final temperature of 32.0°C. The specific heat capacity of water is 4.18 J K^{-1} g^{-1}.

(a) Calculate the number of moles of calcium used. [1]

(b) Calculate the number of moles of acid used. [1]

(c) Write a balanced equation for the reaction. [1]

(d) Hence show that the acid is in excess in the reaction. [1]

(e) Calculate a value for the amount of heat involved in this experiment in kJ. [2]

(f) Convert your answer in part (e) into a value for the enthalpy change, ΔH, in kJ mol^{-1}. [1]

2 For the reaction:

$$I_2(g) + Cl_2(g) \rightarrow 2ICl(g) \qquad \Delta H = -11 \text{ kJ mol}^{-1}$$

If the mean bond energies are $E(I–I)$ = +158 kJ mol^{-1} and $E(Cl–Cl)$ = +242 kJ mol^{-1}, calculate the strength of the I–Cl bond. [3]

3 Calculate the enthalpy of combustion of but-1-ene, $C_4H_8(g)$, given that the enthalpy of formations of but-1-ene, carbon dioxide and water are +1.2, −393.5 and −285.8 kJ mol^{-1} respectively. [3]

4 Table 4.1 gives some values of standard enthalpies of formation ($\Delta_f H^\ominus$).

Table 4.1

Substance	F_2(g)	CF_4(g)	HF(g)
$\Delta_f H^\ominus$/kJ mol^{-1}	0	−680	−269

The enthalpy change for the following reaction is −2889 kJ mol^{-1}.

$$C_2H_6(g) + 7F_2(g) \rightarrow 2CF_4(g) + 6HF(g)$$

Use this value and the standard enthalpies of formation in Table 4.1 to calculate the standard enthalpy of formation of C_2H_6(g). [3]

Answers and quick quiz 4 online

ONLINE

Summary

You should now have an understanding of:
- what is meant by 'enthalpy change'
- how to carry out simple experiments to enable enthalpy changes to be measured
- Hess's law
- enthalpy of formation
- enthalpy of combustion
- how to apply Hess's law by drawing simple energy cycles
- mean bond enthalpies and using them to calculate enthalpy changes

AQA AS/A-level Year 1 Chemistry   43

5 Kinetics

> **Rate of reaction** is defined as the *rate of change of concentration with time*. It can be expressed mathematically in the form:
>
> $$\text{rate of reaction (mol\,dm}^{-3}\,\text{s}^{-1}) = \frac{\text{change in concentration (mol\,dm}^{-3})}{\text{time for concentration change (s)}}$$

Collision theory

Effective collisions

REVISED

For reactions to occur, particles with sufficient energy must collide — the type of collision that leads to a reaction is called an **effective collision**. If particles do not have enough energy for a reaction, or do not collide with the correct alignment or orientation, an **ineffective** or **inelastic collision** may result.

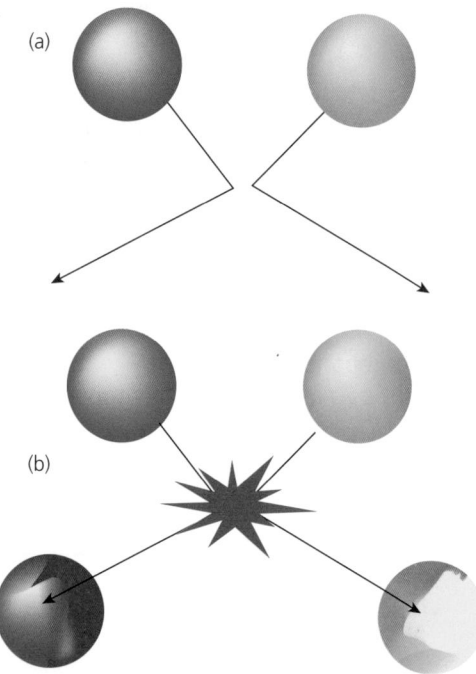

Figure 5.1 Collisions in reactions: (a) ineffective; (b) effective

The **activation energy**, E_a, is the minimum energy required for a reaction to take place. If the combined energy of the particles colliding is less than the activation energy, then a reaction is not likely to occur — this is an ineffective collision. If the combined energy of the particles exceeds the activation energy then an effective collision is more likely.

Most collisions that take place between particles do not lead to a reaction because the combined energy of the particles is lower than the activation energy.

Factors affecting rate of reaction

Changing the temperature

As the temperature increases, so too does the average kinetic energy of the particles in a reaction mixture. Particles will collide with a greater combined energy and if this exceeds the reaction activation energy then a reaction may occur.

The distribution of particles at two different temperatures, T_1 and T_2, can be represented on a **Maxwell–Boltzmann distribution** (Figure 5.2).

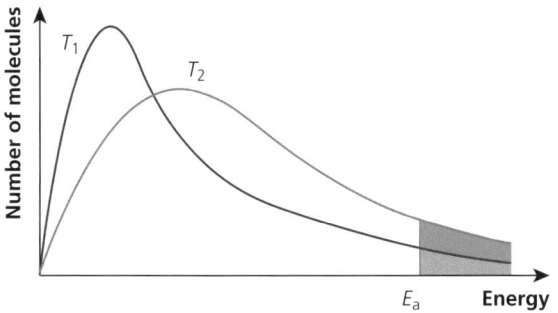

Figure 5.2 Maxwell–Boltzmann distributions at different temperatures

- At the lower temperature, T_1, the proportion of molecules with an energy greater than the activation energy, E_a, is given by the blue-shaded area.
- If the temperature is increased to T_2, a new distribution is formed in which the peak of the graph shifts to higher energy. A *much* greater proportion of particles possess an energy greater than the activation energy — the pink+blue-shaded areas — and therefore there will be a lot more successful collisions at the higher temperature, so the rate of reaction increases dramatically.
- Rate of reaction is normally very sensitive to temperature increases. This is because the proportion of molecules having an energy exceeding the activation energy — the area to the right of E_a — increases dramatically (exponentially) as the temperature increases. A small temperature increase can cause a significant shift of the Maxwell–Boltzmann distribution to the right, therefore moving more molecules to higher energies.

> **Typical mistake**
>
> Many students state that it is the fact that molecules collide more often at a higher temperature that causes the greater rate of reaction. It is because more molecules are colliding with greater *energy*, and therefore sufficient energy to react, that has the much greater effect.

Now test yourself

1 The rate of reaction between hydrogen gas and oxygen gas to form water is sensitive to changes in temperature.

$$2H_2(g) + O_2(g) \rightarrow 2H_2O(l)$$

Suggest why an increase in temperature increases the rate of this reaction.

Answer on p. 102

Changing the concentration

REVISED

Concentration is a measure of the number of particles per unit volume and is normally expressed in $mol\,dm^{-3}$. The greater the concentration, the higher the number of particles per unit volume.

As the concentration of a solution increases, there will be more particles in the same volume. More collisions per unit time will occur and a greater number of effective collisions will take place, giving a greater rate of reaction.

In the left-hand box in Figure 5.3, the concentration of red particles is much lower than that on the right-hand side. This means that fewer collisions place per unit time between the red and blue balls on the left-hand side than on the right. This would give a lower rate of reaction because fewer effective collisions would result.

> **Exam tip**
>
> With gases, as the pressure is increased the concentration of particles also increases. This is analogous to increasing the concentration within a solution.

Figure 5.3 The effect of concentration

Using a catalyst

REVISED

Manganese(IV) oxide is a **catalyst** in the decomposition of hydrogen peroxide:

$$2H_2O_2(aq) \rightarrow 2H_2O(l) + O_2(g)$$

Without the catalyst, the reaction rate would be significantly slower. When manganese(IV) oxide is added, it provides an alternative reaction pathway, or mechanism, by which the reaction can take place. This alternative route is faster, because it has a lower activation energy.

If the activation energy is lowered (Figure 5.4) there will be a greater proportion of particles with an energy exceeding the old activation energy threshold and a faster reaction rate results.

> A **catalyst** is a substance that increases the rate of a reaction by *providing an alternative reaction pathway* with a *lower activation energy*. At the end of the reaction a catalyst is chemically unchanged.

> **Exam tip**
>
> Note that the activation energy is lowered using a catalyst. However, when explaining the effect of temperature and concentration on rate, the activation energy stays the same.

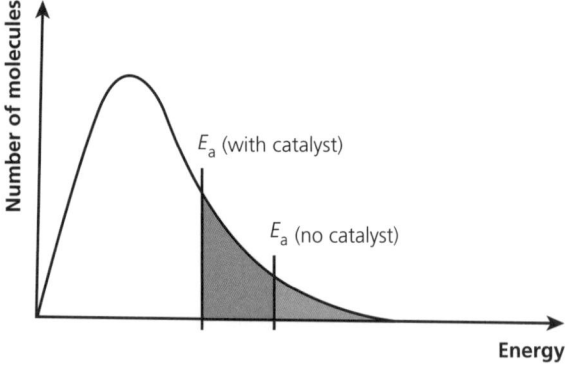

Figure 5.4 The effect of a catalyst on activation energy

You can also sketch an energy profile for a reaction to show how a catalyst affects the activation energy for a process, as shown in Figure 5.5. Note the following about this diagram:
- The activation energy for the uncatalysed reaction is much higher than that for the catalysed reaction.

- The enthalpy change for the reaction is unchanged — a catalyst affects the rate but not the amount of heat absorbed or released.

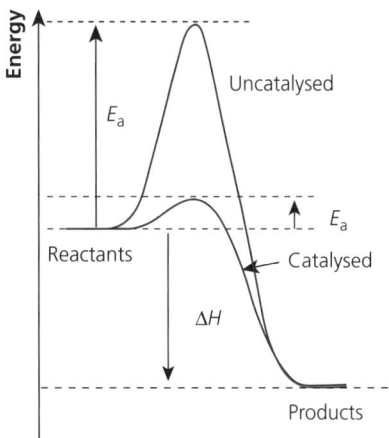

Figure 5.5 Energy profile for a catalysed reaction

Now test yourself

2 The reaction between sodium thiosulfate solution, $Na_2S_2O_3(aq)$, and dilute hydrochloric acid can be represented by:

$$Na_2S_2O_3(aq) + 2HCl(aq) \rightarrow 2NaCl(aq) + S(s) + SO_2(g) + H_2O(l)$$

Explain why the rate of this reaction increases when the concentration of sodium thiosulfate increases.

3 Give an example of a catalyst in use, and explain how it increases the rate of the chemical reaction.

Answers on p. 102

Exam practice

1 (a) Give the meaning of the term 'activation energy'. [1]

Figure 5.6 shows a distribution of molecular energies at a particular temperature. The activation energy is also shown for the reaction.

Figure 5.6

(b) Label on the graph:
- the most common energy [1]
- molecules with the highest energy [1]
- molecules with the lowest energy [1]

(c) On the same axes, draw the graph expected when the reaction mixture is heated by a further 10°C. [2]

(d) Use your graphs to explain why an increase in temperature of 10°C results in an average increase in the rate of reaction by a factor of approximately 2. [2]

2 For the reaction $2HI(g) \rightarrow H_2(g) + I_2(g)$, the activation energy when uncatalysed is $183 \, kJ \, mol^{-1}$ and when catalysed with gold it is $105 \, kJ \, mol^{-1}$. ΔH for the reaction is $-52 \, kJ \, mol^{-1}$.

(a) Sketch an energy profile diagram for the reaction, including the activation energies for both the uncatalysed and catalysed reactions. [2]

(b) Calculate the activation energy for the reverse reaction, $H_2(g) + I_2(g) \rightarrow 2HI(g)$, in both the uncatalysed and catalysed reactions. [2]

(c) Explain why increasing the concentration of hydrogen iodide gas results in a faster reaction rate. [2]

Questions 3 and 4 are about the Maxwell–Boltzmann distribution shown in Figure 5.7.

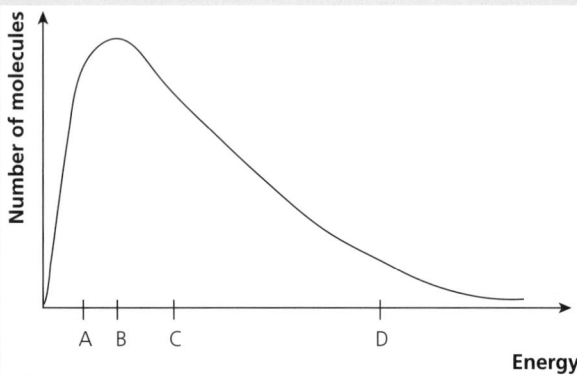

Figure 5.7

3 Which letter best represents the mean energy of the molecules? [1]
4 What does the area under the curve represent? [1]
   A   the total energy of the particles
   B   the total number of particles
   C   the number of particles that can react with each other
   D   the total number of particles that have activation energy

Answers and quick quiz 5 online

ONLINE ▢

Summary

You should now have an understanding of:
- collision theory:
  - particles have to collide to react
  - particles need to possess a certain minimum energy to react

- activation energy
- how temperature affects the rate of reaction
- the Maxwell–Boltzmann distribution
- how concentration affects the rate of reaction
- what is meant by 'catalysts' and how they work

6 Equilibria

The dynamic nature of equilibria

Reversible reactions

There are many reactions that can be described as being 'reversible' — that is, they can proceed in either the forward or reverse directions. For example, ethene can be hydrated to form ethanol, C_2H_5OH:

$$C_2H_4(g) + H_2O(g) \rightarrow C_2H_5OH(l)$$

On the other hand, ethanol can be dehydrated to form ethene and water:

$$C_2H_5OH(l) \rightarrow C_2H_4(g) + H_2O(g)$$

When a reaction that is reversible takes place, both the forward and reverse processes will occur until a **state of dynamic chemical equilibrium** is attained. When the system (reaction) reaches this stage, the rates of the forward and reverse reactions are equal.

When at equilibrium ($\rightleftharpoons$) the reaction above can be represented as:

$$C_2H_4(g) + H_2O(g) \rightleftharpoons C_2H_5OH(g)$$

Another example of making an alcohol in an industrial process is when carbon monoxide reacts with hydrogen to form methanol, CH_3OH:

$$CO(g) + 2H_2(g) \rightleftharpoons CH_3OH(g)$$

A state of equilibrium will occur only if the system is **closed**, so that nothing is allowed to enter or leave the reaction.

> **Exam tip**
>
> When a reaction is at equilibrium, the concentrations of reactants and products are not equal, but the *rates* of the forward and reverse processes are equal.

> **Exam tip**
>
> Both ethanol and methanol are important fuels, and both are formed industrially via equilibrium processes.

The equilibrium constant, K_c

For a reaction at equilibrium, a mathematical expression may be written that relates the equilibrium concentrations of reactants and products to a constant called the equilibrium constant, known as K_c.

When writing an expression for K_c:
- Focus on the product side of the equilibrium first and write each substance as a concentration, using square brackets.
- If there is more than one product, multiply the different concentrations together.
- Raise each concentration to a power, where this power is equal to the number before the substance in the chemical equation.
- Do the same with the reactants, but write this under the products as a division.

For example, in the equilibrium:

$$C_2H_4(g) + H_2O(g) \rightleftharpoons C_2H_5OH(g)$$

the equilibrium constant is given by:

$$K_c = \frac{[C_2H_5OH(g)]}{[C_2H_4(g)][H_2O(g)]}$$

For the reaction below:

$$CO(g) + 2H_2(g) \rightleftharpoons CH_3OH(g)$$

the equilibrium constant is given by:

$$K_c = \frac{[CH_3OH(g)]}{[CO(g)][H_2(g)]^2}$$

What does the equilibrium constant tell us?

The greater the value of K_c, the higher the proportion of products compared with reactants in the mixture at equilibrium, and vice versa. For example, K_c for a reaction may have a very large value of, say, 10^6. This indicates that products dominate in the equilibrium mixture and that the equilibrium position lies to the right-hand side.

Conversely, the value for K_c could be very small, for example, 10^{-6}. This means that reactants dominate the mixture, and the equilibrium position lies largely to the left-hand side.

What doesn't the equilibrium constant tell us?

The rate of reaction is unknown. The constant gives us information about the **final composition** of the equilibrium mixture but not about how long it takes to form. It could take many years to come to equilibrium, or a fraction of a second.

Now test yourself

TESTED ☐

1 Write down equilibrium constant expressions for the following reactions at equilibrium.
   (a) $N_2(g) + 3H_2(g) \rightleftharpoons 2NH_3(g)$
   (b) $H_2(g) + I_2(g) \rightleftharpoons 2HI(g)$
   (c) $N_2(g) + O_2(g) \rightleftharpoons 2NO(g)$

Answer on p. 102

Qualitative effects of changes in external conditions

Equilibrium position

REVISED ☐

Reactions that come to equilibrium will consist of varying relative proportions of reactants and products. If a reaction comes to equilibrium and the quantity of reactants is greater than the quantity of products, the reaction is said to have an equilibrium position that lies on the left-hand side.

The **equilibrium position** therefore gives a measure of the extent to which the reaction takes place, and the position of equilibrium can be 'shifted' by changing the external conditions.

Le Chatelier's principle

Using **Le Chatelier's principle**, it is possible to predict the qualitative effect of changing external conditions — for example, concentration, pressure or temperature — on an equilibrium position.

> **Le Chatelier's principle** states that if the conditions under which an equilibrium exists are changed, the position of equilibrium alters in such a way as to oppose the change in conditions.

Changing the concentration of a reactant or a product

If the concentration of a substance changes, the reaction shifts position so as to oppose the concentration change.

Consider this example. The following process involving the formation of the ester methyl methanoate (CH_3OCHO) has reached equilibrium:

$$CH_3OH(l) + HCOOH(l) \rightleftharpoons CH_3OCHO(l) + H_2O(l)$$

- If the concentration of methanol, CH_3OH, is increased by adding more moles of CH_3OH, the position of equilibrium position moves to lower the concentration of the CH_3OH — it shifts to the *right-hand side* to produce more ester.
- If methanoic acid, HCOOH, is removed from the equilibrium by reducing its concentration, the equilibrium position shifts so as to produce more HCOOH — the equilibrium shifts to the *left-hand side*.

Changing the pressure

If a reaction involves gases, the equilibrium position will be affected by changes in external pressure. Consider the manufacture of ammonia:

$$N_2(g) + 3H_2(g) \rightleftharpoons 2NH_3(g)$$

- There is a total of 4 mol of gas on the left-hand side of the equilibrium and only 2 mol of gas on the right-hand side, so the left-hand side (the reactants) will exert the greater pressure relative to the products.
- If the external pressure is increased, the equilibrium position moves so as to decrease the pressure. The reaction will do this by shifting to the right-hand side to produce more molecules of ammonia and fewer molecules of nitrogen and hydrogen.

However, if the reaction being considered is:

$$H_2(g) + I_2(g) \rightleftharpoons 2HI(g)$$

- A change in external pressure will not affect the equilibrium position because there are equal numbers of moles of gas on each side of the equation.
- The *rate* at which equilibrium is attained will be affected because pressure affects the relative distance between molecules in the gas phase. The collision rate will therefore change and the number of effective collisions will also change.

Changing the temperature

To predict how a change of temperature affects the equilibrium position, the sign of the enthalpy change, ΔH, for the reaction has to be known. Consider the reaction:

$$N_2(g) + O_2(g) \rightleftharpoons 2NO(g) \qquad \Delta H = +180.5\,kJ\,mol^{-1}$$

- The *forward* reaction is *endothermic*. Therefore, formation of NO(g) is accompanied by the removal of heat from the surroundings.

- The *reverse* process is *exothermic*. Heat will be released when $N_2(g)$ and $O_2(g)$ are formed.
- If the external temperature is increased, the reaction will try to remove excess heat by using its forward process and more $NO(g)$ will form.
- Temperature also affects the rates of both the forward and the reverse process (but not equally). If the temperature is increased, the rates of both processes increase and the rate at which the equilibrium is attained also increases.

Catalysts

A **catalyst** will not affect the equilibrium *position*; it will only affect the *rate* at which the equilibrium is attained.

The ester ethyl ethanoate, $CH_3COOC_2H_5$, is formed in this reaction:

$$C_2H_5OH(l) + CH_3COOH(l) \rightleftharpoons CH_3COOC_2H_5(l) + H_2O(l)$$

- It can take a long time for this reaction to come to equilibrium — many months, or even years.
- If a catalyst such as concentrated sulfuric acid is added, the equilibrium is attained faster.
- The rates of the forward and reverse processes are increased equally by the catalyst.

> **Exam tip**
>
> The equilibrium constant, K_c, gives a measure of the resulting equilibrium composition. Changes in concentration, pressure or surface area of a solid, or adding a catalyst, have no effect on the value of K_c. Only temperature will affect its value.

The importance of equilibria in industrial processes

Ethanol production

One very important example of a reversible reaction that comes to a state of dynamic equilibrium is in the industrial manufacture of ethanol from steam and ethene:

$$C_2H_4(g) + H_2O(g) \rightleftharpoons C_2H_5OH(g) \quad \Delta H \text{ } -ve$$

Ethene reacts with steam in the presence of a phosphoric acid catalyst (on a silica support) at 300°C, and a pressure of about 60–70 atm.

The process is reversible and so it is important to appreciate how conditions are changed so that a greater yield of ethanol is formed at an appreciable rate.

Pressure

- **Yield:** in the equation for the process, there are fewer gas molecules (low pressure) on the product side, and more gas molecules (high pressure) on the reactant side. When the external pressure is increased, the equilibrium will shift to the right-hand side to reduce the pressure, so a greater yield of ethanol will form.

- **Rate:** when gases are compressed, there will be more collisions per unit time because the molecules will be closer together. The rate at which equilibrium is achieved therefore increases.

Temperature

- **Yield:** decreasing the temperature will increase the yield of ethanol, because the forward exothermic reaction will be favoured.
- **Rate:** a lower temperature will result in a lower rate of reaction.

A compromise is found between yield and rate by adopting a moderate temperature.

Now test yourself

TESTED

2 Indicate the effect on (a) the equilibrium position and (b) the rate at which equilibrium is attained when the temperature is increased in this equilibrium:

$$2NO_2(g) \rightleftharpoons N_2O_4(g)$$

The forward reaction is exothermic.

(c) Write an expression for K_c for the equilibrium.

Answer on p. 102

> **Exam tip**
>
> Yield and rate are different features of an equilibrium system — Le Chatelier's principle can be used to explain the changes to the yield; collision theory explains the changes to the rate.

Catalyst

The phosphoric acid catalyst affects the rate at which the equilibrium is attained; it does not affect the yield of ethanol formed.

Now test yourself

TESTED

3 Copy and complete Table 6.1 to describe some changes to the following equilibrium:

$$CO(g) + 2H_2(g) \rightleftharpoons CH_3OH(g)$$

The forward reaction is exothermic.

Table 6.1

	Equilibrium position	Rate at which equilibrium is attained
Total pressure is increased		
Temperature is increased		
A catalyst is added		

Answer on p. 102

Exam practice

1 In the Haber process, nitrogen and hydrogen react in the presence of an iron catalyst to form ammonia according to the equation:

$N_2(g) + 3H_2(g) \rightleftharpoons 2NH_3(g)$

(a) The production of ammonia is accompanied by heat being released. Explain whether a low temperature or a high temperature would result in the higher yield of ammonia being formed. [2]

(b) State what happens to the rate at which equilibrium is attained when:
  (i) the temperature is increased [1]
  (ii) the pressure is decreased [1]

(c) Explain your answers to part (b) in terms of energies of particles. [2]

(d) Explain why a moderately high temperature of 450°C is used when manufacturing ammonia industrially. [2]

(e) Explain why pressures of more than 200–350 atm are rarely used in the Haber process. [2]

(f) In one particular year, the USA produced 8 million tonnes of ammonia at a cost of $200 per tonne.
  (i) Calculate the total cost of the US production of ammonia. [1]
  (ii) Calculate the mass of nitrogen gas required to produce 8 million tonnes of ammonia. [A_r data: N = 14; H = 1] [2]

(g) Given that the process produces an overall ammonia yield of 15%, calculate the mass of nitrogen required when this is taken into account. [1]

2 Colourless solutions of X(aq) and Y(aq) react to form an orange solution of Z(aq) according to the following equation:

$X(aq) + 2Y(aq) \rightleftharpoons Z(aq)$ $\Delta H = -20\,kJ\,mol^{-1}$

A student added a solution containing 0.50 mol of X(aq) to a solution containing 0.50 mol of Y(aq) and shook the mixture. After 30 seconds, there was no further change in colour. The amount of Z(aq) at equilibrium was 0.20 mol.

(a) Deduce the amounts of X(aq) and Y(aq) at equilibrium. [2]

(b) The student prepared another equilibrium mixture in which the equilibrium concentrations of X and Z were: X(aq) = 0.40 mol dm^{-3} and Z(aq) = 0.35 mol dm^{-3}. For this reaction, the equilibrium constant $K_c = 2.9\,mol^{-2}\,dm^6$. Calculate a value for the concentration of Y at equilibrium. Give your answer to the appropriate number of significant figures. [3]

(c) The student added a few drops of Y(aq) to the equilibrium mixture of X(aq), Y(aq) and Z(aq) in part (b). Suggest how the colour of the mixture changed. Give a reason for your answer. [3]

Answers and quick quiz 6 online

ONLINE

Summary

You should now have an understanding of:
- reversible reactions
- what is meant by 'state of equilibrium'
- what is meant by 'dynamic equilibrium'
- how Le Chatelier's principle can be used to predict the direction in which an equilibrium shifts when external conditions are changed

- writing an expression for K_c for a given equilibrium
- the production of ethanol in terms of how to change external conditions to optimise both yield and rate

7 Redox reactions

Oxidation and reduction

Redox reaction

REVISED

In a **redox reaction**, one substance is **oxidised** and another is **reduced**. The substance that oxidises the other is called an **oxidising agent**. The substance that reduces the other substance is called the **reducing agent**.

A simple redox reaction takes place when a metal compound, like aluminium oxide, is electrolysed. These processes take place at the electrodes:
- at the (−) cathode: $Al^{3+} + 3e^- \rightarrow Al$
- at the (+) anode: $2O^{2-} \rightarrow O_2 + 4e^-$

Aluminium ions gain electrons, so they are **reduced**.

Oxide ions lose electrons, so they are **oxidised**.

> **Oxidation** is the loss of electrons.
>
> **Reduction** is the gain of electrons.

Oxidation states

Working out the oxidation state

REVISED

An oxidation state is a number indicating the 'formal' charge that an element would have in a compound if the compound were ionic. The oxidation state of an element is zero.

Working out the oxidation state for an element in a compound assumes that all the other oxidation states are known. The sum of all of the oxidation states in a compound is zero.

Some typical oxidation states:
- hydrogen (except when in hydrides) = +1
- group 1 metals = +1
- group 2 metals = +2
- oxygen (except when in hydrogen peroxide) = −2
- fluorine = −1

> **Example**
>
> Work out the oxidation state of the following:
> (a) iron in Fe_2O_3
> (b) manganese in $KMnO_4$
> (c) chromium in $Na_2Cr_2O_7$
>
> Answer
>
> (a) In Fe_2O_3 the known oxidation state is oxygen at –2.
>   Therefore, $2Fe + 3(-2) = 0$
> $2Fe = +6$, so each iron $= +3$
>   This compound is called iron(III) oxide, where 'III' is the oxidation state of the iron in the compound.
> (b) In $KMnO_4$ the known oxidation states are potassium at +1 and oxygen at –2.
>   Therefore, $(+1) + Mn + 4(-2) = 0$
> $Mn = (+8) - 1$, so each manganese $= +7$
>   The compound is called potassium manganate(VII), where 'VII' is the oxidation state of manganese in the compound.
> (c) In $Na_2Cr_2O_7$ the known oxidation states are sodium at +1 and oxygen at –2.
>   Therefore, $2(+1) + 2Cr + 7(-2) = 0$
> $2 + 2Cr - 14 = 0$, so $2Cr = 14 - 2$
> $Cr = +6$, so each chromium $= +6$
>   This compound is called sodium dichromate(VI), where 'VI' is the oxidation state of chromium in the compound.

For complex ions such as SO_4^{2-}, the sum of the oxidation states is equal to the charge on the ion.

> **Example**
>
> What is the oxidation state of aluminium in the ion $[AlF_6]^{3-}$?
>
> Answer
>
> Known oxidation states: $F = -1$
>
> Therefore, $Al + 6(-1) = -3$
>
> $Al - 6 = -3$
>
> So $Al = -3 + 6 = +3$

Now test yourself

TESTED

1 What is the oxidation state of the named element in each of these compounds and ions?
  (a) cobalt in $CoCl_3$
  (b) chlorine in $NaOCl$
  (c) titanium in $TiCl_4$
  (d) iron in Na_2FeO_4
  (e) sulfur in H_2SO_4
  (f) iodine in IO_3^-
  (g) manganese in MnO_4^{2-}
2 Name, using oxidation states, the compounds in question 1.

Answers on p. 102

Using oxidation states

When carrying out a reaction, it is possible to deduce whether the reaction is redox or not, and if it is, which elements have been oxidised and which reduced.

Exam tip

If the oxidation state of an element increases, this is an **oxidation**. If it decreases this is a **reduction**.

> **Example**
>
> Determine whether the following are redox reactions or not by deducing the oxidation state changes.
> (a) H_2SO_4(l) + NaCl(s) → $NaHSO_4$(s) + HCl(g)
> (b) $2SO_2$(g) + O_2(g) + $2H_2O$(l) → $2H_2SO_4$(aq)
>
> Answer
>
> (a) H_2SO_4: hydrogen = +1; oxygen = −2, so sulfur = +6
>   NaCl: sodium = +1; chlorine = −1
> $NaHSO_4$: sodium = +1; hydrogen = +1; oxygen = −2, so sulfur = +6
>   HCl: hydrogen = +1; chlorine = −1
>   So all the oxidation states before and after the reaction are the same, so this reaction is not a redox reaction.
> (b) SO_2: sulfur = +4; oxygen = −2
> O_2: oxygen = 0
> H_2O: hydrogen = +1 and oxygen = −2
> H_2SO_4: hydrogen is +1, sulfur is +6 and oxygen is −2.
>   Hydrogen's oxidation state stays the same.
>   Sulfur changes oxidation state from +4 to +6. It has been oxidised.
>   Oxygen (starting in O_2) changes from 0 to −2. It has been reduced.
>   The reaction is therefore a redox reaction.

Now test yourself

TESTED

3 Deduce the names of the oxidising and reducing agents in the reaction:

$2SO_2$(g) + O_2(g) + $2H_2O$(l) → $2H_2SO_4$(aq)

4 Show that the reaction below is a redox reaction by determining the oxidation states of the elements that change. Also deduce the names of the oxidising and reducing agents:

PbO_2(s) + 4HCl(aq) → $PbCl_2$(aq) + $2H_2O$(l) + $2Cl_2$(g)

Answers on p. 103

Redox equations

Writing half-equations

REVISED

Redox reactions consist of two separate processes — an oxidation and a reduction. These can be written separately in the form of **half-equations**.

Example

Magnesium metal is added to copper(II) sulfate solution to form copper and magnesium sulfate solution. Write a balanced symbol equation for the reaction and also the half-equations. Then determine which element has been oxidised and which has been reduced.

Answer

$$Mg(s) + CuSO_4(aq) \rightarrow MgSO_4(aq) + Cu(s)$$

In this reaction, the magnesium atoms lose two electrons to form magnesium ions, Mg^{2+}.

Half-equation: $Mg(s) \rightarrow Mg^{2+}(aq) + 2e^-$

The magnesium atoms have therefore been oxidised.

The copper(II) ions, Cu^{2+}, gain two electrons to form copper atoms, Cu.

Half-equation: $Cu^{2+}(aq) + 2e^- \rightarrow Cu(s)$

The copper(II) ions have therefore been reduced.

Now test yourself

TESTED

5 Write two half-equations that take place in the reactions between:
   (a) zinc and iron(II) sulfate solution
   (b) aluminium and copper(II) sulfate solution

Answers on p. 103

The two half-equations in the example above can be combined to form an overall **ionic equation**:

$$Cu^{2+}(aq) + Mg(s) \rightarrow Mg^{2+}(aq) + Cu(s)$$

When oxidation and reduction half-equations are combined, the electrons *must* cancel out.

In this reaction, magnesium has been oxidised and the copper(II) ion is the **oxidising agent**, because it caused this oxidation. Copper(II) ions are reduced, and so magnesium is called the **reducing agent**.

Example

Given the following half-equations for a redox reaction between chlorine and bromide ions, combine them together to produce an overall ionic equation:

$$Cl_2 + 2e^- \rightarrow 2Cl^-$$

$$2Br^- \rightarrow Br_2 + 2e^-$$

Answer

Adding these two together, and cancelling the electrons on each side, gives:

$$Cl_2 + 2Br^- \rightarrow Br_2 + 2Cl^-$$

> **Example**
>
> When lithium metal is added to water, reactions occur according to these two half-equations:
>
> $$Li \rightarrow Li^+ + e^-$$
>
> $$2H_2O + 2e^- \rightarrow 2OH^- + H_2$$
>
> What is the balanced equation for the reaction?
>
> **Answer**
>
> Multiplying the first equation by 2 to balance the electrons, then adding and cancelling the electrons gives:
>
> $$2Li + 2H_2O \rightarrow 2Li^+ + 2OH^- + H_2$$
>
> So the required equation is $2Li + 2H_2O \rightarrow 2LiOH + H_2$.

Exam practice

1 Nitrogen dioxide reacts with water:

$$2NO_2(g) + H_2O(l) \rightarrow H^+(aq) + NO_3^-(aq) + HNO_2(aq)$$

   (a) Give the oxidation states of nitrogen in all the nitrogen-containing species in the equation. [3]
   (b) Which substance has been oxidised in the reaction? [1]
2 Scrap iron can be used to extract copper from dilute aqueous solutions containing copper(II) ions. Write the simplest ionic equation for the reaction of iron with copper(II) ions in aqueous solution. [1]
3 Ammonia reacts with oxygen in the presence of a platinum catalyst to form nitrogen(II) oxide and steam.
   (a) Write a balanced equation for the reaction. [2]
   (b) Identify which substances have been reduced and oxidised in the reaction. [2]
   (c) What is the name of the reducing agent in the process? [1]
4 Which of the following shows chlorine in its correct oxidation states in the compounds shown? [1]

	HCl	KClO$_3$	HClO
A	−1	+3	+1
B	+1	−5	−1
C	−1	+5	+1
D	+1	+5	−1

Answers and quick quiz 7 online

ONLINE

Summary

You should now have an understanding of:
- what is meant by oxidation and reduction in terms of electron transfer
- what is meant by a redox reaction
- oxidation state
- how to deduce the oxidation state for an element in a compound

- how to use oxidation states to determine which elements have been oxidised and reduced in a reaction
- half-equations and how to write them for simple reactions
- how to combine half-equations to give ionic equations for redox reactions

8 Periodicity

Periodicity is the regular and **repeating pattern** of various physical or chemical properties. Since the outer electronic configuration of atoms is a periodic function, we therefore expect other properties to change accordingly.

Classification of elements in s, p, d or f blocks

The periodic table

The periodic table is an arrangement of the known chemical elements according to their atomic numbers.

Elements are put into vertical columns called **groups**, in which all elements have similar chemical properties, as well as horizontal rows called **periods**.

Elements are classified as either s-, p-, d- or f-block elements according to their position in the periodic table. For example, group 1 and 2 elements are in the s block (Figure 8.1) and their outer, highest-energy electrons occupy the *s*-sublevel.

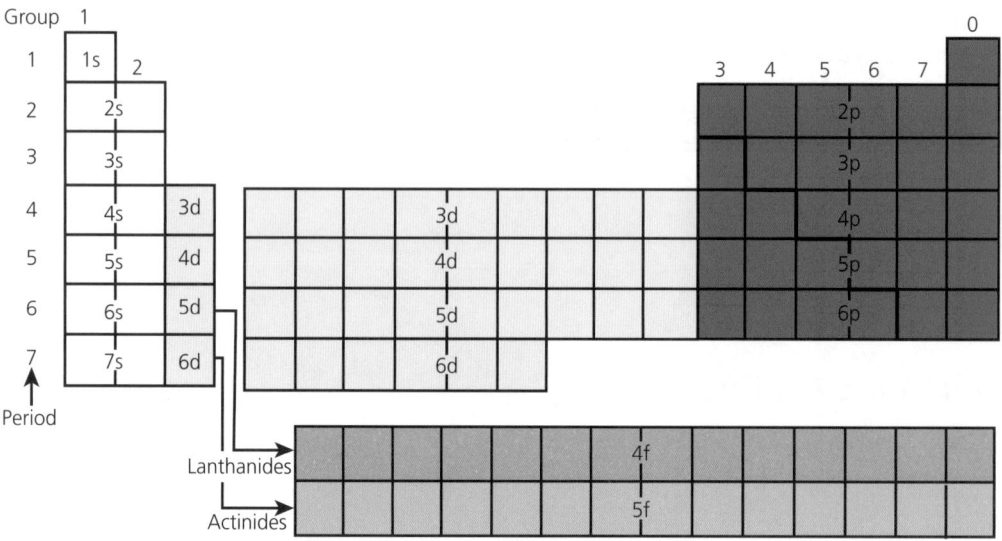

Figure 8.1 The s, p, d and f blocks in the periodic table

Now test yourself

1 In which block of the periodic table are the elements in groups 7 and 0 to be found?
2 The electronic configuration of boron, B, is $1s^2, 2s^2, 2p^1$. In which block of the periodic table would you expect boron be to be found?

Answers on p. 103

Properties of the period 3 elements

Atomic radius

Figure 8.2 shows atomic radius plotted against atomic number for periods 2, 3 and 4 in the periodic table. A regular repeating pattern is seen; this is an example of periodicity.

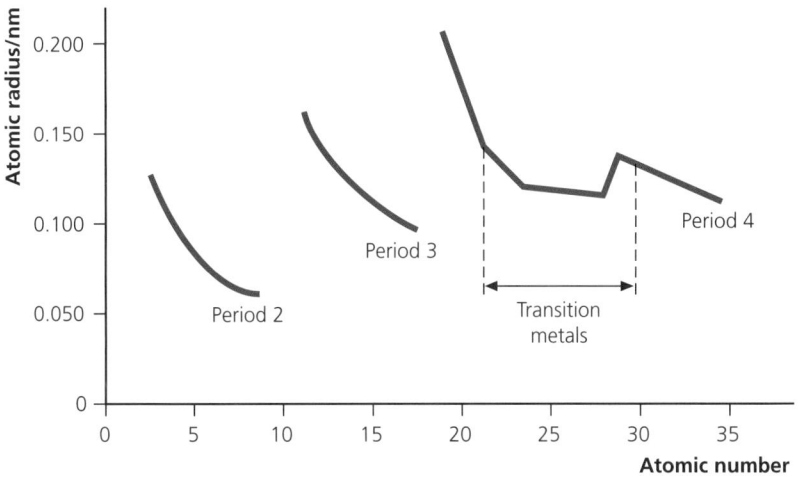

Figure 8.2 Graph of atomic radius versus atomic number

The graph shows two main trends.

Across a period

Moving from left to right across a period, the atomic radius generally decreases.

As the atomic number increases, the number of protons in the nucleus increases. Electrons are also being added, and to the same energy level. There is a greater electrostatic attraction between the outer electrons and the nucleus and so the atomic radius decreases.

Down a group

Electrons are being added to a higher energy level, progressively further from the nucleus. There is a reduction in the electrostatic attraction because of the increasing distance and so the atomic radius increases.

First ionisation energy

Figure 1.4 on page 11 shows how the first ionisation energy changes with atomic number. Chapter 1 outlines the evidence for electron energy levels and sublevels, and gives an explanation of the ionisation energy trends observed down the groups and across a period.

Melting and boiling points

On moving across the periodic table from left to right along period 3, there is a gradual change in structure of the solid element (Table 8.1). When explaining the trends in melting and boiling points, it is important to know how the structures change.

Table 8.1 Element structures in period 3

Group	1	2	3	4	5	6	7	0
Element	Na	Mg	Al	Si	P	S	Cl	Ar
Structural type	Giant metallic			Giant covalent	Simple covalent			Individual atoms

Figure 8.3 shows how the general trend seen in the melting points of the elements across a period relates closely to the trend seen in structure.

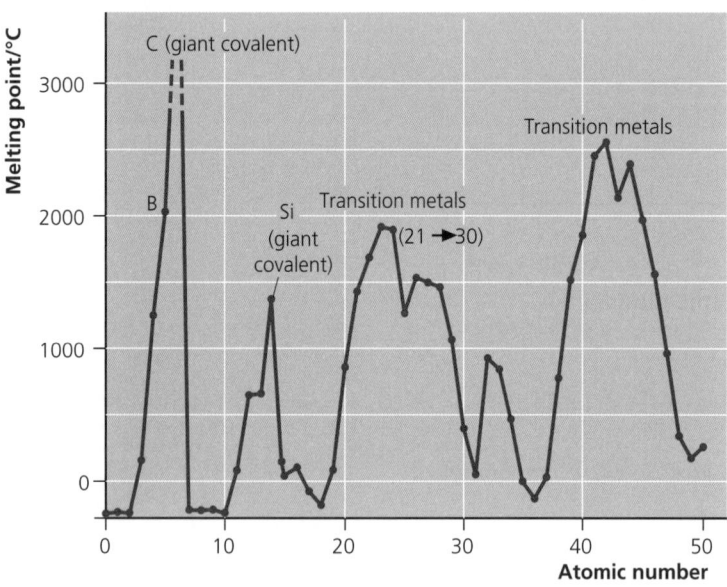

Figure 8.3 Graph of melting point versus atomic number

> **Revision activity**
>
> Using the internet, find the boiling points of the period 2 elements (lithium to neon) and then plot them on a graph to see that the same pattern is seen as with the melting points.

- The melting and boiling points of metals increase from group 1 through to group 3. This is because there are more electrons being delocalised into the **giant metallic structure**, and so there will be a greater electrostatic attraction between the positive ions and the mobile electrons. For example, the attraction between Al^{3+} ions and three electrons (on average) will be greater than that between Na^+ ions and one electron. It will therefore be more difficult to separate the ions from each other in the melting or boiling process.
- The group 4 element has the highest melting and boiling point in period 3. Silicon atoms are strongly covalently bonded throughout in a **giant covalent structure** similar to that of diamond, so it will be difficult to melt or boil the element because this will involve breaking strong covalent bonds.
- There is a large drop after silicon but from then to the end of the period the melting point depends only on van der Waals forces, which in turn depend on the size of the molecules involved. In group 5, phosphorus consists of separate P_4 molecules in a **simple covalent structure**. These molecules will be relatively easy to separate because their weak van der Waals forces will be easy to overcome. Sulfur in group 6 consists of S_8 molecules, chlorine in group 7 consists of Cl_2

molecules, and argon in group 0 consists of separate atoms. Larger molecules with more electrons, for example S_8, give rise to larger van der Waals forces and hence their melting and boiling points are higher because it requires more energy to separate the molecules from each other.

Now test yourself

3 Explain the following:
   (a) Why does sodium have a larger atomic radius than magnesium?
   (b) Why does aluminium have a lower first ionisation energy than magnesium?
   (c) Why does sulfur have a higher boiling point than chlorine?

Answer on p. 103

Exam practice

1 An element X has the following first six ionisation energies in $kJ\,mol^{-1}$:
   577, 1820, 2740, 11 600, 14 800, 18 400
   (a) Explain how you know that element X is in group 3 of the periodic table. [1]
   (b) Element Y is in the same group as element X, but it is placed in the period below X in the periodic table.
      (i) Give an approximate value for the first ionisation energy of element Y. [1]
      (ii) Explain, using ideas of electronic structure, why you expect element Y to have this ionisation energy. [2]
   (c) Two elements W and Z are in the same period as X, but W is in the group before X, and Z is in the group after X in the periodic table.
      (i) Give approximate first ionisation energies for elements W and Z. [2]
      (ii) Explain, using ideas of electronic structure, why elements W and Z have these ionisation energies. [2]
2 Indicate the general trend in the following properties across a period from group 1 to group 8:
   (a) (i) first ionisation energy [1]
      (ii) atomic radius [1]
   (b) Explain the variation in melting points across a period. [2]
3 Explain these observations:
   (a) Sodium has a larger atomic radius than lithium. [2]
   (b) Silicon has a higher melting temperature than phosphorus, P_4. [2]
4 Which of these atoms has the highest electronegativity? [1]
   A Na
   B Mg
   C Cl
   D Ar
5 Which of these atoms has the largest atomic radius? [1]
   A Ar
   B Cl
   C Mg
   D Na

Answers and quick quiz 8 online

Summary

You should now have an understanding of:
- what is meant by the term 'periodicity'
- how elements can be classified in s, p, d or f blocks in the periodic table
- how atomic radius, first ionisation energy and melting and boiling point can be used to demonstrate periodicity

9 The periodic table

Group 2: the alkaline earth metals

The elements in group 2 — beryllium, magnesium, calcium, strontium, barium and radium — are all metals.

Trends in physical properties

Atomic radius

The atomic radius *increases* down the group, as shown in Figure 9.1.

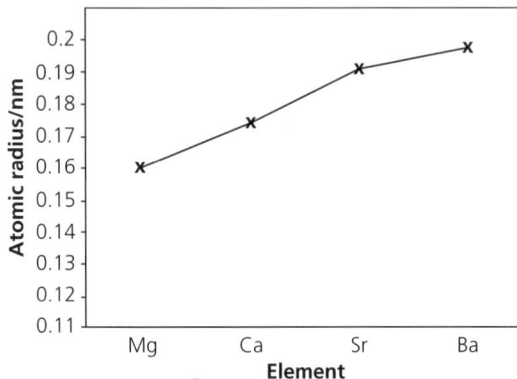

Figure 9.1 Atomic radii of group 2 elements

- The number of electron energy levels increases down the group.
- The outer electrons experience more shielding.
- There will be a weaker electrostatic attraction between the outer electrons and the nucleus.
- So the atomic radius will increase.

Melting points of the elements

As Figure 9.2 shows, the general trend in melting point is for this to *decrease* down the group.

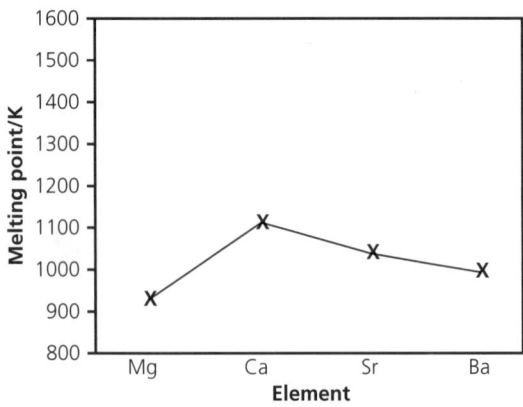

Figure 9.2 Melting points of group 2 elements

Magnesium's melting point does not fit the general trend because it has a different metallic structure from the other elements in the group.

- All the elements are metals, so the structure of all these elements is **giant metallic**.
- Each atom donates two electrons to the delocalised electrons in the giant metallic structure.
- Ions of charge +2 form in the structure and these are bonded electrostatically by the mobile electrons.
- As the group is descended, the radius of the +2 ion increases because there are more electron energy levels.
- The outer electrons are further from the nucleus of each ion, and therefore further from the delocalised mobile electrons.
- The strength of the metallic bonding therefore decreases, and the melting point falls.

First ionisation energy of the elements

As Figure 9.3 shows, the first ionisation energy *decreases* down the group.

> The **first ionisation energy** is the energy required to remove 1 mol of electrons from 1 mol of gaseous atoms under standard conditions:
>
> $$M(g) \rightarrow M^+(g) + e^-$$

Figure 9.3 First ionisation energy of group 2 elements

- There are more electron energy levels as the group is descended.
- The outer electron being removed is progressively further from the nucleus
- There will be less electrostatic attraction between the outer electron being removed and the nucleus.
- Therefore, the first ionisation energy will decrease.

Reactions of group 2 elements

REVISED

All the metals in group 2 are reactive, but not as reactive as group 1 metals. They all react by losing their outer two *s*-electrons to form a positive ion (a cation) with a +2 charge.

Reaction with water

Group 2 metals react with cold water according to the general equation (where M is the group 2 metal):

$$M(s) + 2H_2O(l) \rightarrow M(OH)_2(aq) + H_2(g)$$

A solution of the metal hydroxide (a weak base) forms along with hydrogen gas.

Reactivity *increases* down the group as it becomes progressively easier to remove two electrons because both the distance and the shielding between the outer electrons and the nucleus increase.

So the reactivity order for the metals, based on their rate of reaction with water is:

$$Mg \ll Ca < Sr < Ba$$

> **Example**
>
> Write equations for the reactions of barium and magnesium with cold water. Comment on any differences in the observed rates of reaction.
>
> **Answer**
> - barium: $Ba(s) + 2H_2O(l) \rightarrow Ba(OH)_2(aq) + H_2(g)$
> - magnesium: $Mg(s) + 2H_2O(l) \rightarrow Mg(OH)_2(aq) + H_2(g)$
>
> The reaction of magnesium with water is much slower than that of barium. In fact, magnesium reacts only very slowly with cold water.

- The metal hydroxide that forms becomes more soluble as the group is descended.
- Because the hydroxide is more soluble as the group is descended, the concentration of hydroxide ions in solution will also be higher. The alkalis that are formed are stronger.
- The order of the relative solubility of the metal hydroxides and their strength as soluble bases (alkalis) is:

$$Mg(OH)_2 < Ca(OH)_2 < Sr(OH)_2 < Ba(OH)_2$$

- Magnesium hydroxide is used as an antacid in medicine — it reacts with excess acid in the stomach and relieves indigestion. Calcium hydroxide is used in agriculture because it neutralises excess acidity in soil. Both uses exploit the compound's ability to react as a base.

Group 2 metals also react with steam, in which the reaction rate is considerably faster than that with cold water. Magnesium reacts violently with steam, as shown below:

$$Mg(s) + H_2O(g) \rightarrow MgO(s) + H_2(g)$$

Group 2 sulfates

Down the group, the sulfates become less soluble. The order of solubility is:

$$MgSO_4 > CaSO_4 > SrSO_4 > BaSO_4$$

When magnesium sulfate is added to water, a colourless solution is formed. When barium sulfate is added to water, almost none dissolves because it is extremely insoluble.

The **test for sulfate(VI) ions**, SO_4^{2-}, is to add hydrochloric acid and barium chloride solution. A white precipitate of barium sulfate(VI) will result. Hydrochloric acid is added to decompose any carbonate that may be present. A carbonate will also form a white precipitate with barium chloride solution and confuse the observations being made.

- Barium sulfate(VI), $BaSO_4$, is an insoluble compound and is easy to observe when **testing for a sulfate** because it forms a thick white precipitate.
- If sodium sulfate(VI) is the substance being tested, the reaction will be:

$$Na_2SO_4(aq) + BaCl_2(aq) \rightarrow BaSO_4(s) + 2NaCl(aq)$$

The **ionic equation** will be:

$$Ba^{2+}(aq) + SO_4^{2-}(aq) \rightarrow BaSO_4(s)$$

Exam practice answers and quick quizzes at **www.hoddereducation.co.uk/myrevisionnotes**

- Barium sulfate is used in medicine when examining a patient's digestive system. The patient drinks a chalky barium sulfate suspension. When the patient is X-rayed, the barium sulfate coating inside the digestive tract absorbs a large proportion of the radiation. This highlights the black-and-white contrast of the X-ray photograph, so that doctors can diagnose digestive problems better.

Now test yourself

1 Write an equation to show how calcium reacts with water. What would be observed in this reaction?
2 Describe a chemical test that would enable you to distinguish between sodium nitrate and sodium sulfate.

Answers on p. 103

Group 7: the halogens

- The halogens are fluorine (F), chlorine (Cl), iodine (I), bromine (Br) and astatine (At) — they are members of group 7 of the periodic table.
- All halogens exist as diatomic molecules at room temperature and pressure, and are often given the general symbol X_2.

Trends in physical properties

Boiling point

Boiling points *increase* down the group.
- The number of electrons in each molecule is increasing.
- This increases the number and strength of the **van der Waals interactions** between molecules.
- So it becomes harder to separate one molecule from another.

At room temperature fluorine is a pale-yellow gas, chlorine is a pale-green gas, bromine is an orange liquid and iodine is a dark-grey solid. Figure 9.4 shows clearly that the melting points and boiling points increase regularly down the group.

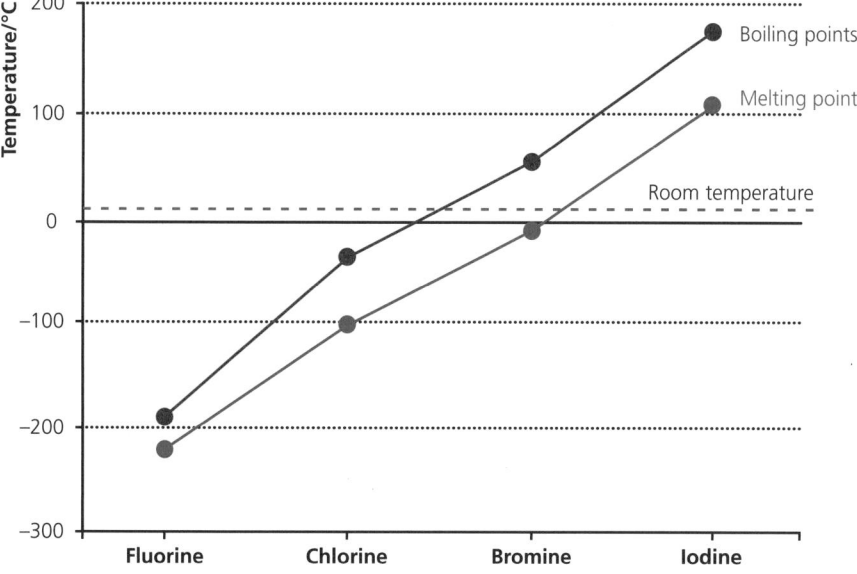

Figure 9.4 Melting and boiling points of group 7 elements

Electronegativity

Electronegativity *decreases* down the group.
- The atomic radius increases because of the added electron shells.
- Therefore the bonding pair of electrons in the covalent bond gets progressively further from the positively charged nucleus. There will also be additional shielding.
- This means that there will be less electrostatic attraction between the nucleus and the bonding electron pair as the group is descended, and the electronegativity decreases.

> **Exam tip**
>
> Remember that the term 'electronegativity' refers to the ability of an atom to attract pairs of **bonding** electrons in covalent bonds.

Trends in the oxidising ability of halogens

REVISED

Halogen molecules, X_2, react by gaining electrons from other substances. A half-equation to show this process would be $X_2 + 2e^- \rightarrow 2X^-$.

In this process, the halogen molecule has been **reduced** because it has gained electrons. The other substance has been **oxidised** because it has had electrons removed by the halogen. This is why halogens are **oxidising agents**.

For example, sodium reacts with chlorine according to:

$$2Na(s) + Cl_2(g) \rightarrow 2NaCl(s)$$

Chlorine oxidises the sodium from oxidation state 0 to +1. Chlorine itself is reduced and changes oxidation number from 0 to −1.

The **oxidising power** of the halogens *decreases* down the group.
- As the group is descended, the number of electron energy levels increases.
- The distance between the outer electron shell and the nucleus (the atomic radius) increases.
- Shielding increases between the outer shell electrons and the nucleus.
- Because of the extra distance and shielding, the larger atoms attract an extra electron less strongly.
- Hence the oxidising power decreases down the group, and also the ability of a halogen molecule to be reduced.

Halogen–halide displacement reactions

A more reactive halogen will displace a less reactive halogen from its compounds.

When chlorine gas, $Cl_2(g)$, is bubbled through a solution containing sodium bromide, $NaBr(aq)$, a **redox reaction** occurs in which the chlorine **oxidises** the bromide ions to aqueous bromine, $Br_2(aq)$.
- The overall equation for the reaction is $2NaBr(aq) + Cl_2(g) \rightarrow 2NaCl(aq) + Br_2(aq)$.
- The half-equation to show bromide ions being oxidised is $2Br^- \rightarrow Br_2 + 2e^-$.
- The half-equation to show chlorine molecules being reduced is $Cl_2 + 2e^- \rightarrow 2Cl^-$.
- The order of oxidising power of halogens is: $F_2 > Cl_2 > Br_2 > I_2$ (ignoring astatine).
- The order of reducing power of halide ions is: $I^- > Br^- > Cl^- > F^-$.
- Fluorine is a powerful oxidising agent and can oxidise Cl^-, Br^- and I^-.
- Chlorine can oxidise Br^- and I^-. Bromine can only oxidise I^-.

> **Exam tip**
>
> Make sure that you use the correct words — 'chlorine' for the molecular element and 'chloride' for the ion.

Exam practice answers and quick quizzes at **www.hoddereducation.co.uk/myrevisionnotes**

Now test yourself

3 Explain why chlorine is a more powerful oxidising agent than iodine.
4 (a) Give an equation that shows how bromine reacts with sodium iodide solution.
  (b) Which substance is oxidised and which is reduced in this reaction?

Answers on p. 103

Trends in the reducing ability of halide ions

REVISED ☐

Halide ions increase in **reducing power** as the group is descended.

● There are more electron energy levels as the group is descended.
● The **ionic radius** of the halide ion increases.
● The amount of shielding between the outer electrons and the nucleus increases.
● There is a lower electrostatic attraction between the nucleus and the electrons.
● So it is easier to remove an electron from a halide ion as the group is descended.
● Therefore, **halide ions** are more readily oxidised — they are more powerful reducing agents.

The changing reducing ability of the halide ions can be demonstrated using a reaction between a halide salt and concentrated sulfuric acid.

Using NaCl(s):

> sodium + concentrated → sodium hydrogen + hydrogen
> chloride   sulfuric acid   sulfate(vi)   chloride gas
>
> $NaCl(s)$ + $H_2SO_4(l)$ → $NaHSO_4(s)$ + $HCl(g)$

Using NaBr(s), and ignoring the Na^+ spectator ion:

> $Br^- + H_2SO_4 \rightarrow HSO_4^- + HBr$

then:

> $2HBr + H_2SO_4 \rightarrow Br_2 + SO_2 + 2H_2O$

Using NaI(s):

> $I^- + H_2SO_4 \rightarrow HSO_4^- + HI$

then:

> $8HI + H_2SO_4 \rightarrow 4I_2 + H_2S + 4H_2O$

● In the first stage, the halide ion is protonated by the concentrated sulfuric acid:

> $X^- + H^+ \rightarrow HX$

● If a bromide or an iodide is used, a second stage occurs in which the sulfuric acid is reduced.
● The oxidation state of sulfur in sulfuric acid is +6. This is reduced to +4 in SO_2 and −2 in H_2S.
● The iodide ion is the most powerful reducing agent of the halide ions and produces a mixture of products including SO_2, S and H_2S in the reaction with sulfuric acid.

> **Typical mistake**
>
> Many students write an equation showing the formation of sodium sulfate(vi), Na_2SO_4. It is sodium *hydrogen*sulfate(vi) that forms when concentrated sulfuric acid is used.

Now test yourself

5 Write an equation to show how potassium fluoride reacts with concentrated sulfuric acid.
6 (a) What are the different oxidation states of sulfur in H_2S, SO_2 and S?
  (b) Write an equation for the reaction between hydrogen iodide and concentrated sulfuric acid to form sulfur, iodine and water.

Answers on p. 103

Identification of halide ions using silver nitrate

Halide ions, X^-, can be identified using silver nitrate solution acidified with nitric acid. Nitric acid is used in the halide ion test because it reacts with any carbonates that may be present before silver nitrate is added. Silver ions react with carbonate ions to form white silver carbonate, and this will confuse the test.

> ### Example
>
> Using calcium chloride, an addition of acidified silver nitrate solution produces a white precipitate of silver chloride:
>
> $$CaCl_2(aq) + 2AgNO_3(aq) \rightarrow Ca(NO_3)_2(aq) + 2AgCl(s)$$
>
> Write an ionic equation for the reaction.
>
> #### Answer
>
> $Ag^+(aq) + Cl^-(aq) \rightarrow AgCl(s)$

The silver halide precipitates have similar colours and can be difficult to tell apart. A further test using aqueous ammonia of different concentrations can distinguish between them.

Table 9.1 Distinguishing silver halides

Silver halide formed	Colour of precipitate	Solubility in dilute $NH_3(aq)$	Solubility in concentrated $NH_3(aq)$
Silver chloride, AgCl(s)	White	Soluble — a colourless solution forms	Soluble — a colourless solution forms
Silver bromide, AgBr(s)	Cream	Insoluble	Soluble — a colourless solution forms
Silver iodide, AgI(s)	Yellow	Insoluble	Insoluble

> ### Example
>
> A solution of a substance Y is acidified with nitric acid and then a few drops of aqueous silver nitrate are added. A cream precipitate is formed. The precipitate is insoluble in dilute ammonia solution and does dissolve in concentrated ammonia.
>
> What can you deduce from this information?
>
> #### Answer
>
> You can deduce that bromide ions must have been present in the compound, because the precipitate was cream in colour and dissolved in concentrated ammonia, but not in dilute ammonia.

> ### Revision activity
>
> Prepare some flashcards, on one side writing the type of halogen reaction (for example 'displacement with halide ions') and on the reverse writing the chemical equations that you must know.

Uses of chlorine and chlorate(I) compounds

Reaction of chlorine with water

Chlorine reacts with water according to the equation:

chlorine + water → chloric(I) acid + hydrochloric acid

$Cl_2(g) + H_2O(l) \rightarrow HOCl(aq) + HCl(aq)$

- The chloric(I) acid formed, $HOCl(aq)$, is a powerful oxidising agent. Chlorine is in oxidation state +1.
- In the above reaction, the chlorine initially is in oxidation state 0. At the end of the reaction, chlorine is in oxidation state +1 in chloric(I) acid (an oxidation); in hydrochloric acid it is in oxidation state −1 (a reduction).
- The powerful oxidising nature of chloric(I) acid is exploited in using chlorine to purify water supplies for drinking.
- Although chlorine is poisonous, its benefits in killing microorganisms responsible for water-borne diseases, such as cholera, typhoid and diphtheria, outweigh any potential disadvantages.
- Chloric(I) acid, $HOCl(aq,)$ is a bleaching and oxidising agent, and it decomposes in the presence of sunlight to form oxygen:

$2HOCl(aq) \rightarrow 2HCl(aq) + O_2(g)$

> **Typical mistake**
>
> Many students know that chlorine is added to water to disinfect it; but few understand that its action is due to the oxidising nature of the chloric(I) acid formed.

Reaction of chlorine with cold, aqueous, dilute sodium hydroxide solution

Chlorine disproportionates in cold, dilute and aqueous alkali:

$Cl_2(g) + 2NaOH(aq) \rightarrow NaOCl(aq) + NaCl(aq) + H_2O(l)$

- Chlorine's oxidation state increases from 0 to +1 and also decreases from 0 to −1. The product of this reaction, sodium chlorate(I) (NaOCl), is used as a **bleach** and as a **disinfectant** to kill germs.
- The chlorate(I) ion **oxidises** germs and bacteria by removing electrons:

$ClO^-(aq) + 2H^+(aq) + 2e^- \rightarrow Cl^-(aq) + H_2O(l)$

Now test yourself

7 Describe a chemical test to distinguish between lithium chloride and lithium iodide. Write ionic equations for the reactions that take place.

8 (a) Give different uses for chlorine and sodium chlorate(I).
  (b) Give reagents for a reaction in which chloric(I) acid forms.

Answers on p. 103

Exam practice

1 Concentrated sulfuric acid is added separately to potassium chloride and potassium iodide.
  (a) Write equations to show each of the reactions. [2]
  (b) Predict two expected observations when potassium astatide (KAt) is added to concentrated sulfuric acid. [2]
  (c) Explain these trends down group 7 using the electronic structures of the atoms to help you:
    (i) electronegativity [2]
    (ii) boiling point [2]
    (iii) atomic radius [2]
  (d) Write equations for these reactions involving halogens or halide ions:
    (i) potassium with fluorine gas [2]
    (ii) sodium bromide solution with chlorine gas [2]
    (iii) chlorine gas with water [2]
    (iv) sodium chloride solution with silver nitrate solution [2]
2 (a) Give uses for these substances: [4]
    (i) calcium hydroxide, $Ca(OH)_2$
    (ii) magnesium hydroxide, $Mg(OH)_2$
    (iii) chlorine, Cl_2
    (iv) barium sulfate(VI), $BaSO_4$
  (b) Describe chemical tests to distinguish between each of the compounds in these pairs:
    (i) potassium iodide and potassium bromide [3]
    (ii) copper(II) chloride and copper(II) sulfate [3]
3 State and explain the trend in the first ionisation energies of the elements in group 2 from magnesium to barium. [3]
4 Which of these elements has the highest second ionisation energy? [1]
  A Na
  B Mg
  C Ne
  D Ar

Answers and quick quiz 9 online

ONLINE

Summary

You should now have an understanding of:
- how atomic radius, melting point and first ionisation energy vary down group 2 of the periodic table
- reactions of group 2 metals with water
- the variation in the solubility of group 2 hydroxides
- how to test for sulfate(VI) ions using acidified barium chloride solution
- the variation in solubility of group 2 sulfates

- how electronegativity, melting point and boiling point vary down group 7 of the periodic table
- the oxidising power of the halogens
- halogen–halide displacement reactions
- the relative reducing power of the halides shown in their reactions with halogens and with concentrated sulfuric acid
- how to test for a halide ion using acidified silver nitrate solution
- how chlorine reacts with water and cold, dilute, aqueous sodium hydroxide

10 Alkanes

Fractional distillation of crude oil

Alkanes are **hydrocarbons** — this means that their molecules contain *only* hydrogen and carbon atoms. The general formula of an alkane is C_nH_{2n+2}.

Alkanes are **saturated** — this means that they contain only carbon–carbon single bonds — no multiple bonds.

The alkanes are found in crude oil and are separated from this by a process called **fractional distillation**. Crude oil is a complex mixture of mainly hydrocarbons. The complex mixture can be separated into smaller mixtures or fractions that have different boiling points. These different components of the mixture can be drawn off at different levels in a fractionating column because of the temperature gradient up the column (Figure 10.1).

Low temperature

70°C → Petroleum gases

→ Naphtha (gasoline)

→ Kerosene (paraffin)

→ Diesel

→ Lubricating oil

Crude oil is heated and enters the column as a gas

→ Heavy fuel oil

High temperature

360°C → Bitumen

Figure 10.1 Fractional distillation of crude oil

Formulae and naming

Formulae

The first five members of the alkane **homologous series** are shown in Figure 10.2.

methane   ethane   propane

butane   pentane

Figure 10.2 The first five alkanes

Because they form a homologous series:
- they have the same general formula
- they contain the same functional groups and have similar chemical properties
- each member differs from the next by a CH_2 unit

The **molecular formula** gives the atoms of each element in a molecule. The **empirical formula** gives the simplest whole number ratio of atoms of each element in a molecule.

Using butane as an example:
- the **displayed formula** showing all the bonds is
- the **structural formula** is $CH_3CH_2CH_2CH_3$
- the **molecular formula** is C_4H_{10} — this shows the actual number of atoms of each element in the molecule, but shows no structure
- the **empirical formula** is C_2H_5 — this shows the simplest whole-number ratio for the numbers 4 and 10 in the molecular formula

$$H-\overset{\overset{\displaystyle H}{|}}{C}-\overset{\overset{\displaystyle H}{|}}{\underset{\underset{\displaystyle H}{|}}{C}}-\overset{\overset{\displaystyle H}{|}}{\underset{\underset{\displaystyle H}{|}}{C}}-\overset{\overset{\displaystyle H}{|}}{\underset{\underset{\displaystyle H}{|}}{C}}-H$$

Now test yourself

TESTED

1 Write the displayed formula, structural formula, molecular formula and empirical formula for *n*-hexane, C_6H_{14}.

Answer on p. 103

> **Exam tip**
>
> Ensure that you understand the differences between the types of formula — they can sometimes be very different.

Naming alkanes

REVISED

Unbranched alkanes are easy to name because they follow the 1: meth-, 2: eth-, 3: prop-, 4: but- system with -ane at the end of the name. For example, the alkane containing a longest chain of three carbon atoms is called propane.

Branched-chain alkanes are named according to the following steps:
1 Find the longest continuous chain of carbon atoms.
2 Look for any branches along the longest chain — how many carbons atoms are there in each branch and at what positions are they along the longest chain?

> **Exam tip**
>
> The arrangement around each carbon atom is actually tetrahedral. When the structures are 'squashed' onto a flat page, the angles look like 90° or 180°, but they are all 109.5°.

> **Example**
>
> Name the molecules in Figure 10.3.
>
> (a)   (b)
>
> Figure 10.3
>
> **Answer**
>
> (a) It has four carbon atoms in its longest chain.
>   It has one methyl group positioned at the number 2 carbon atom (counting from the shortest end).
>   Name: 2-methylbutane
> (b) It has six carbon atoms in its longest chain.
>   It has two methyl groups and they are both at the number 2 position.
>   Name: 2,2-dimethylhexane

Now test yourself

2 Name the alkanes in Figure 10.4, all of which are isomers of C_5H_{12}.

(a)

$CH_3-CH_2-CH_2-CH_2-CH_3$

(b)

$$CH_3-\overset{\overset{\displaystyle CH_3}{|}}{CH}-CH_2-CH_3$$

(c)

$$CH_3-\overset{\overset{\displaystyle CH_3}{|}}{\underset{\underset{\displaystyle CH_3}{|}}{C}}-CH_3$$

Figure 10.4

Answers on p. 103

Isomerism

Structural isomers

REVISED

Many organic molecules, like alkanes, can form more than one structure with the same number or atoms in each molecule — these are called **isomers**.

There are several different types of structural isomerism — **chain**, **position** and **functional group**.

> **Structural isomers** are molecules with the same molecular formula but different structural formulae.

Chain isomerism

REVISED

These isomers arise because of the possibility of branching in carbon chains. For example, there are two isomers of C_4H_{10}. In one of them, the carbon atoms lie in a 'straight' chain whereas in the other the chain is branched (Figure 10.5).

butane

2-methylpropane

Figure 10.5

Position isomerism

REVISED

In position isomerism, the basic carbon skeleton remains unchanged, but important groups are attached to different carbon atoms along the chain (Figure 10.6).

$CH_3-CH_2-CH_2-Br$

1-bromopropane

$$CH_3-\overset{\overset{\displaystyle }{}}{\underset{\underset{\displaystyle Br}{|}}{CH}}-CH_3$$

2-bromopropane

Figure 10.6

Functional group isomerism

REVISED

In this type of structural isomerism, the isomers contain different functional groups — that is, they belong to different families of compounds (different homologous series). For example, a molecular formula C_3H_6O could be either propanal (an aldehyde) or propanone (a ketone) (Figure 10.7).

propanal   propanone

Figure 10.7

Cracking of alkanes

Breaking carbon–carbon bonds

Longer-chain alkanes are not as marketable as the smaller and more useful alkanes. Because of this low demand, the larger molecules are **thermally** or **catalytically cracked** to form both higher-value alkanes and alkenes.

Cracking involves breaking of carbon–carbon bonds in an alkane, and so energy is required to make this happen. It is the process by which long-chain alkanes are converted into smaller alkanes and, normally, alkenes.

For example, the alkane decane, $C_{10}H_{22}$, could be cracked as follows:

$$C_{10}H_{22}(g) \rightarrow C_8H_{18}(g) + C_2H_4(g)$$

> **Catalytic cracking** involves using a slightly increased pressure and a high temperature — a **zeolite catalyst** is often used. Aromatic hydrocarbons and motor fuel are two of the important products formed in this catalytic cracking process.
>
> **Thermal cracking** involves using a high temperature at high pressure. This process produces a high percentage of **alkenes**.

Now test yourself

TESTED

3 Write an equation to show the cracking of the alkane nonane, C_9H_{20}, to form ethene and one other product.

Answer on p. 103

> **Exam tip**
>
> Cracking often produces ethene, C_2H_4, which is used to make the polymer poly(ethene).

Combustion of alkanes

Fuels

Alkanes are often used as fuels when burned in oxygen. The products formed depend on the amount of oxygen gas available. For example, propane gas, C_3H_8, can be combusted in excess oxygen — complete combustion: $C_3H_8(g) + 5O_2(g) \rightarrow 3CO_2(g) + 4H_2O(l)$

Alternatively it can burn by partial or incomplete combustion, in which the oxygen supply is limited: $C_3H_8(g) + \frac{7}{2}O_2(g) \rightarrow 3CO(g) + 4H_2O(l)$

> **Exam tip**
>
> Note that water is always formed in hydrocarbon combustion. However, carbon monoxide or carbon can be formed when the oxygen supply is limited.

Now test yourself

TESTED

4 If $100\,cm^3$ of ethane is combusted completely, what volume of oxygen is required to ensure that this happens? Assume that all volumes are measured under the same conditions.
5 Write an equation to show the incomplete combustion of methane in which gases are formed.

Answers on p. 103

Environmental issues

In a typical car engine in which diesel or petrol is the fuel, carbon monoxide, unburned hydrocarbons and oxides of nitrogen (NO_x) gases are found in exhaust gases — all of these are potential pollutants and can present a problem to human health.

Pollutants such as nitrogen monoxide, $NO(g)$, and carbon monoxide, $CO(g)$, are removed from car exhaust fumes using a catalytic converter.

The gases react *together* on the surface of a catalyst, such as rhodium, palladium or platinum, to form products that are less harmful:

$$2NO(g) + 2CO(g) \rightarrow 2CO_2(g) + N_2(g)$$

If fuels contain sulfur, then sulfur dioxide will form when the fuel is burned. This gas is acidic and contributes to acid rain. It can be removed by passing it through powdered calcium oxide (a base) so that it reacts. An acid–base neutralisation occurs: $CaO(s) + SO_2(g) \rightarrow CaSO_3(s)$

Gases, such as carbon dioxide and water vapour, and unburned hydrocarbons, such as methane, are all **greenhouse gases**. This means that they are able to absorb infrared radiation, which results in the temperature of the atmosphere increasing. This is called **global warming**.

Now test yourself

TESTED

6 Give the names of two chemical pollutants that are formed when a fuel such as petrol is combusted. How are these pollutants removed?

Answer on p. 103

Exam practice

1 The alkane pentane is a saturated hydrocarbon.
  (a) (i) State the meaning of the terms 'saturated' and 'hydrocarbon' as applied to alkanes. [2]
     (ii) Give the general formula for the alkanes. [1]
  (b) Pentane burns completely in oxygen.
     (i) Write an equation for this reaction. [1]
     (ii) State how the product of this reaction may affect the environment. [1]
  (c) Give the name of the solid pollutant that may form when pentane burns incompletely in air. [1]
  (d) A molecule of $C_{13}H_{28}$ can be cracked to propene and one other product.
     (i) Write an equation for this cracking reaction. [1]
     (ii) Suggest a type of compound that can be manufactured from the propene produced in this cracking reaction. [1]
     (iii) State why a high temperature is required for cracking reactions to occur. [1]

2 What is the total volume of gas remaining after $20\,cm^3$ of ethane is burned completely in $100\,cm^3$ oxygen? All volumes are measured at the same pressure and the same temperature, which is above 100°C. [1]

$$C_2H_6 + 3\tfrac{1}{2}O_2 \rightarrow 2CO_2 + 3H_2O$$

  A $40\,cm^3$ B $100\,cm^3$ C $120\,cm^3$ D $130\,cm^3$

Answers and quick quiz 10 online

ONLINE

Summary

You should now have an understanding of:
- what the alkanes are
- the terms 'empirical formula', 'molecular formula', 'structural formula' and 'displayed formula'
- homologous series and functional groups
- how to name simple alkanes containing up to six carbons

- what is meant by 'isomers' and, in particular, the various types of structural isomer
- the fractional distillation of crude oil
- the cracking of long-chain alkanes and uses for the products
- the different types of combustion of alkanes
- the consequences of combustion in terms of pollution and how some pollutants are removed

11 Halogenoalkanes

Halogenoalkanes can be classed as **primary**, **secondary** or **tertiary** depending on how many alkyl groups (methyl-, ethyl-, propyl-) are attached to the carbon atom that is bonded to the halogen atom. The halogenoalkanes shown in Figure 11.1 are classed as primary, secondary and tertiary respectively.

> **Halogenoalkanes** are organic molecules based on alkanes in which one or more of the hydrogen atoms have been replaced by halogen atoms.

$H_3C - CH_2 - I$

iodoethane

2-bromopropane

2-chloro-2-methylpropane

Figure 11.1 Examples of halogenoalkanes

Synthesis of chloroalkanes

Chloroalkanes are compounds in which some hydrogen atoms of alkanes have been replaced by one or more chlorine atoms.

Methane with chlorine

Methane, CH_4, reacts with chlorine, Cl_2, in the presence of ultraviolet light in a reaction **mechanism** called **free-radical substitution**.

The overall equation for the reaction is:

$CH_4 + Cl_2 \rightarrow CH_3Cl + HCl$

The mechanism occurs in three stages.

- **Initiation:** chlorine **radicals** are formed in the presence of ultraviolet light:

  $Cl_2 \rightarrow 2Cl\bullet$

- **Propagation:** chlorine radicals react with methane molecules to form new radicals and molecules. Adding the propagation steps together gives the overall equation for the reaction:

  $CH_4 + Cl\bullet \rightarrow HCl + \bullet CH_3$

  then:

  $\bullet CH_3 + Cl_2 \rightarrow CH_3Cl + Cl\bullet$

- **Termination:** radicals react with each other to form molecules:

  $\bullet CH_3 + Cl\bullet \rightarrow CH_3Cl$ or $\bullet CH_3 + \bullet CH_3 \rightarrow C_2H_6$

> **Radicals** are molecules, atoms or ions that have an unpaired electron. This makes them very reactive.

Further substitutions, in which more hydrogen atoms are replaced by halogens, are possible. Using excess alkane will limit this happening.

Halogenoalkanes, like chloroalkanes and chlorofluoroalkanes, can be used as solvents.

Exam practice answers and quick quizzes at **www.hoddereducation.co.uk/myrevisionnotes**

Ozone depletion

Ozone gas, O_3, is formed in the upper atmosphere of our planet. It protects life on Earth from potentially harmful ultraviolet radiation from the Sun.

Chlorine radicals, Cl•, react with ozone resulting in its removal or depletion. Chlorine radicals are formed in the upper atmosphere from halogenoalkanes containing C–Cl bonds, for example the chlorofluorocarbon (CFC) dichlorodifluoromethane, CCl_2F_2. The reaction involves a sequence of initiation and propagation steps.

- **Initiation:** formation of chlorine radicals from the CFC in the presence of ultraviolet light:

$$CCl_2F_2 \rightarrow \text{•}CClF_2 + Cl\text{•}$$

- **Propagation:** reaction of chlorine radicals with ozone molecules:

$$Cl\text{•} + O_3 \rightarrow ClO\text{•} + O_2$$

then:

$$ClO\text{•} + O_3 \rightarrow 2O_2 + Cl\text{•}$$

Adding these two propagation equations gives the overall equation for the reaction:

$$2O_3 \rightarrow 3O_2$$

Chlorine radicals catalyse the decomposition of ozone. Notice how they are used up in the reaction and then reproduced at the end, this being typical catalytic behaviour. This means that chlorine radicals can continue to destroy ozone for many years.

Hydrofluorocarbons, HFCs, and hydrochlorofluorocarbons, HCFCs, are now being used as alternatives to CFCs. However, HCFCs can still deplete the ozone layer. Although their depleting effect is only about one-tenth that of CFCs, serious damage is still being caused. HCFCs are a short-term fix until better replacements can be developed.

Now test yourself

TESTED

1 (a) Explain why CFCs are damaging to the ozone layer.
  (b) State what is meant by a 'radical'.
  (c) Give two equations to show how chlorine radicals attack ozone.
2 Ethane gas reacts with bromine in the presence of ultraviolet light. Bromoethane is one of the products of the reaction.
  (a) Write an overall equation for the main reaction taking place.
  (b) Name the mechanism by which the reaction takes place.
  (c) Outline the mechanism for the reaction.

Answers on p. 103

Nucleophilic substitution

Polar molecules

Halogenoalkanes are **polar molecules**. They contain electronegative halogen atoms, X, that are attached to carbon atoms and the bond is polarised:

$$^{\delta+}C\text{–}X^{\delta-}$$

Halogenoalkanes can react by having their carbon–halogen bond broken. The ease of this breaking depends on the strength of the covalent bond. They can react with **nucleophiles** in which the halogen atom is replaced by a nucleophile.

In the case of **nucleophilic substitution**, a **nucleophile** attacks the slightly positively charged carbon atom. The halogen atom then is substituted by the nucleophile.

Common nucleophiles include: hydroxide, $:OH^-$; cyanide, $:CN^-$ and ammonia, $:NH_3$.

The ease of carbon–halogen bond breaking is:

$$C\text{–}I > C\text{–}Br > C\text{–}Cl > C\text{–}F$$

Therefore, iodoalkanes react faster than other halogenoalkanes because the C–I bond is the weakest.

The order of reactivity is:

iodoalkanes > bromoalkanes > chloroalkanes > fluoroalkanes

Nucleophilic substitution reactions are highly important in organic synthesis because replacing a halogen atom with another functional group is useful and convenient.

> A **nucleophile** is a donor of a lone pair of electrons.

> **Typical mistake**
>
> It is a common misconception for students to explain the rate of reaction of halogenoalkanes with nucleophiles in terms of C–X bond polarity, when it is in fact *bond strength* that is key.

Reaction with aqueous sodium hydroxide solution

Halogenoalkanes undergo substitution reactions with hot, aqueous sodium hydroxide solution in which the $:OH^-$ ion from the alkali acts as a **nucleophile** (lone-pair donor) and attacks the carbon atom attached to the halogen, which is lost as a halide ion (Figure 11.2). For example, using chloromethane:

$$CH_3Cl + OH^- \rightarrow CH_3OH + Cl^-$$

Figure 11.2 The nucleophilic substitution of chloromethane by hydroxide ions

In this reaction, the hydroxide ion nucleophile donates a lone pair of electrons to the carbon atom with the $\delta+$ charge in the halogenoalkane. This is shown using a 'curly arrow' in the mechanism. The two bonding electrons in the carbon–halogen bond then move onto the halogen atom, and a halide ion forms, again shown by a curly arrow.

Reaction with sodium cyanide

Cyanide ions, $:CN^-$, from sodium cyanide act as nucleophiles towards halogenoalkanes:

$$CH_3I + CN^- \rightarrow CH_3CN + I^-$$

The mechanism for this process (Figure 11.3) is identical to the previous cases, using hydroxide ions, OH^-:

Figure 11.3 Cyanide ions reacting with iodomethane

The reaction with ethanolic ammonia

An ammonia molecule acts as a nucleophile and donates its lone pair of electrons to the carbon atom attached to the halogen (Figure 11.4). For example:

$$C_2H_5Br + 2NH_3 \rightarrow C_2H_5NH_2 + NH_4Br$$

The ethylamine that forms is a base and reacts with hydrogen bromide (an acid) to form ammonium bromide. This reaction requires ethanol as a solvent and needs an excess of ammonia to limit further substitution.

Figure 11.4 The nucleophilic reaction between ammonia and bromoethane

Elimination

Elimination reactions

When potassium hydroxide solution, KOH(aq), is added to 2-bromopropane, a nucleophilic substitution reaction in which the hydroxide ion acts as a nucleophile can happen:

$$CH_3-CHBr-CH_3 + OH^- \rightarrow CH_3-CH(OH)-CH_3 + Br^-$$

However, it is also possible for the hydroxide ion to behave as a **base** — a proton is removed from one of the carbon atoms next to the carbon attached to the halogen atom. In this case, an **elimination reaction** takes place, forming an alkene (Figure 11.5).

Figure 11.5 Mechanism to show an elimination process

Exam tip

The choices of solvent and temperature have a crucial role in this type of reaction. A hot ethanol solvent promotes elimination; warm aqueous conditions promote nucleophilic substitution.

The solvent, ethanol, promotes the elimination process over the nucleophilic substitution process.

The products of this reaction are propene, water and bromide ions:

$$CH_3-CHBr-CH_3 + {}^-OH \rightarrow CH_3-CH=CH_2 + Br^- + H_2O$$

Exam practice

1 (a) Name the halogenoalkanes in Figure 11.6. [4]

(i)   (ii)   (iii)   (iv)

Figure 11.6

  (b) Classify the halogenoalkanes in part (a) as primary, secondary or tertiary. [4]
  (c) How are the four molecules related? [1]
  (d) Draw structural formulae to show the products formed when 1-iodobutane reacts with:
     (i) excess ammonia in ethanol [1]
     (ii) warm NaOH(aq) [1]
     (iii) NaCN [1]
  (e) Draw the structure of the product in part (d)(ii) if hot ethanol were used as the solvent. [2]
  (f) How would the rates of reaction differ when chloroethane and bromoethane are reacted separately with aqueous sodium hydroxide solution? Explain your answer. [2]

2 (a) CCl_4 is an effective fire extinguisher but it is no longer used because of its toxicity and its role in the depletion of the ozone layer. In the upper atmosphere, a bond in CCl_4 breaks and reactive species are formed. Identify the condition that causes a bond in CCl_4 to break in the upper atmosphere. Deduce an equation for the formation of the reactive species. [2]
  (b) One of the reactive species formed from CCl_4 acts as a catalyst in the decomposition of ozone. Write two equations to show how this species acts as a catalyst. [2]
  (c) A small amount of freon, CF_3Cl, with a mass of 1.78×10^{-4} kg escaped from a refrigerator into a room of volume 100 m^3. Assuming that the freon is evenly distributed throughout the air in the room, calculate the number of freon molecules in a volume of 500 cm^3. Give your answer to the appropriate number of significant figures. The Avogadro constant = 6.02×10^{23} mol^{-1}. [3]

3 Which of these substances reacts most rapidly to produce a silver halide precipitate with acidified silver nitrate? [1]
  A CH_3Br
  B CH_3Cl
  C CH_3F
  D CH_3I

Answers and quick quiz 11 online

ONLINE

Summary

You should now have an understanding of:
- how methane reacts with chlorine in the presence of ultraviolet light
- the free-radical substitution process
- how ozone is depleted by the presence of chlorine radicals
- nucleophilic substitution mechanisms

- how halogenoalkanes react with NaOH, KCN and excess NH_3
- how a hydroxide ion can behave either as a nucleophile or a base and how the products differ depending on the conditions used
- elimination processes involving halogenoalkanes

12 Alkenes

Structure, bonding and reactivity

Carbon–carbon double bonds

Alkenes are hydrocarbons that contain carbon–carbon double bonds. For this reason they are described as being **unsaturated**.

The presence of a double bond makes alkenes *more reactive* than alkanes. This is because the double bond is an area of high electron density in the molecule.

The structure of the carbon double bond is shown in Figure 12.1.

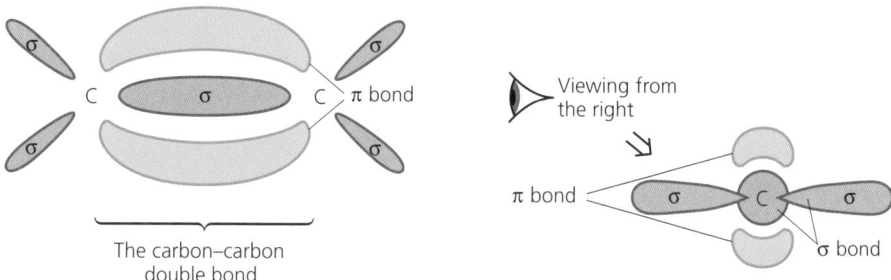

Figure 12.1 Representation of the σ and π bonds in a double bond

- The carbon–carbon double bond arrangement is **planar** (flat) and the internal bond angle is 120°.
- The presence of the π bond prevents rotation about the σ bond.
- This lack of rotation gives rise to **E–Z (geometrical) isomers**.
- *E–Z* geometrical isomerism is one example of **stereoisomerism**.

The *E–Z* isomers in Figure 12.2 show how molecules such as but-2-ene and 1,2-dichloroethene can exist in more than one form. A pair of *E–Z* isomers differ because of the different arrangement of groups in space.

> **Stereoisomers** are compounds with the same structural formula but with bonds arranged differently in space.

Figure 12.2 Geometric isomers

The letter '*E*' indicates that the groups are on opposite sides of the double bond, and '*Z*' shows that they are on the same side.

Now test yourself

1 The alkene pent-2-ene shows *E–Z* (geometrical) isomerism. Draw the displayed formulae of the two stereoisomeric forms.

Answer on p. 104

The Cahn-Ingold-Prelog for assigning *E–Z* stereoisomers

Some molecules containing carbon double bonds have substituents that are all different. How do we decide whether they are *E* or *Z* isomers in these cases?

Method

1 Assign an atomic number to the atom that is directly attached to the carbon atom of the carbon double bond
2 Note down which two atoms have the greater atomic number — these are the important atoms that are given a priority. Sometimes, the atoms may be the same — for example, with $-CH_2OH$ and $-CH_2CH_2OH$. In this case, the next bonded atom counts; here oxygen ($Z = 8$) has a higher priority than carbon ($Z = 6$).
3 Which side of the carbon double bond are the priority atoms? If they are on the same side, then it is a *Z* isomer. If they are on opposite sides, then it is an *E* isomer.

Look at the molecules in Figure 12.3. The two priority groups are those of the greater atomic number — chlorine ($Z = 17$) and bromine ($Z = 35$).

Z-2-bromochloropropene   *E*-2-bromochloropropene

Figure 12.3

The isomer on the left is *Z* (or *cis*) as the bromine and chlorine atoms are on the same side of the double bond. However, the molecule on the right has these two atoms on opposite sides, so it is an *E* (or *trans*) isomer.

Now test yourself

TESTED

2 Deduce whether the molecules in Figure 12.4 are *E* or *Z* geometrical isomers using the Cahn-Ingold-Prelog priority rules.

Figure 12.4

Answer on p. 104

Addition reactions of alkenes

Electrophilic addition

Alkenes react with other substances in a process known as **addition**.

In these reactions, the electron pair present in the π bond of the double bond is donated to the attacking species to form a new single σ bond. The attacking species is therefore an electron pair acceptor, or **electrophile**.

> An **electrophile** is an acceptor of a lone pair of electrons.

The mechanism that describes reactions of this type is called **electrophilic addition**.

Bromine, Br_2, reacts with an alkene in this way. For example, ethene, C_2H_4, reacts with bromine to form 1,2-dibromoethane:

$$H_2C=CH_2 + Br-Br \rightarrow H_2CBr-CH_2Br$$
1,2-dibromoethane

The mechanism by which this reaction takes place is shown in Figure 12.5.

Figure 12.5 An electrophilic addition reaction

The reaction of bromine with an alkene is used as a chemical test for unsaturation. In this test, the colour changes from *orange* to *colourless*.

> **Exam tip**
>
> The use of bromine as a test for a carbon–carbon double bond is one of the most important chemical tests you need to know.

Reactions of alkenes

Alkenes undergo many reactions — for example, the reaction with bromine just mentioned — the other key ones are as follows.

Hydrogen bromide, HBr

Hydrogen bromide *adds* to the double bond in the same way that bromine does, via an **electrophilic addition** process. For example, ethene, C_2H_4, reacts with hydrogen bromide to form bromoethane, C_2H_5Br:

$$H_2C=CH_2 + H-Br \rightarrow H_3C-CH_2Br$$

In this mechanism (Figure 12.6), the first step involves protonation of the carbon–carbon double bond to form a **carbocation**. In the second step, the bromide ion attacks the carbocation.

Figure 12.6 Electrophilic addition of HBr to ethene

If hydrogen bromide is added to an unsymmetrical alkene, such as propene, two products can form: 1-bromopropane or 2-bromopropane (Figure 12.7). This is because either carbon atom can be protonated in the first step of the mechanism, leaving the bromide ion free to bond to either of the resulting **carbocations**.

Figure 12.7 Electrophilic addition of HBr to propene

However, primary carbocations are less stable than secondary carbocations and so the latter are formed preferentially. The bromide ion therefore reacts to form 2-bromopropane as the major product.

Example

Draw the product expected when but-1-ene reacts with hydrogen bromide.

Answer

But-1-ene is shown below. The carbon atom coloured red is attached to fewer hydrogen atoms than the other carbon atom in the double bond:

$$H_2C=CH-CH_2CH_3$$

In the product, this atom will be bonded to the bromine and the hydrogen will be bonded to the other carbon from the double bond. $H_3C-CHBr-CH_2CH_3$, 2-bromobutane, is the major product. This is formed via the more stable secondary carbocation (Figure 12.8).

Figure 12.8

Now test yourself

3 (a) Draw the structure of 2-methylpropene.
   (b) Draw the structures of the two carbocations that could form when 2-methylpropene reacts with hydrogen bromide.
   (c) Which of the carbocations in (b) will be the more stable?
   (d) Hence draw the structure of the major product expected in the reaction.

Answer on p. 104

Sulfuric acid

Alkenes react with concentrated sulfuric acid at 0°C in an electrophilic addition process. The products are hydrogensulfates:

$$C_2H_4 + H_2SO_4 \rightarrow H_3C-CH_2-OSO_3H$$
Ethyl hydrogensulfate

The product is formed via a carbocation intermediate (Figure 12.9), the same as in the reaction with hydrogen bromide.

Figure 12.9 Electrophilic addition of H_2SO_4 to ethene

The product reacts with water — a process called hydrolysis — to form an **alcohol**. For example, ethyl hydrogensulfate forms ethanol:

$$H_3C-CH_2-OSO_3H + H_2O \rightarrow C_2H_5OH + H_2SO_4$$

Alcohols are produced industrially by the reaction of steam with an alkene in the presence of an acid catalyst. This process is called **hydration**.

Conditions used are 300°C and 60–70 atm, with phosphoric(v) acid as a catalyst. For example, ethanol can be made by the hydration of ethene using steam:

$$C_2H_4(g) + H_2O(g) \rightarrow C_2H_5OH(g)$$

> **Revision activity**
>
> There are several alkene reactions you need to know. Why not test your understanding by drawing the structure of any alkene, and then drawing the products that this molecule would form with HBr, Br_2, H_2SO_4 and then water.

Polymerisation

Addition polymers

REVISED

Alkenes will **polymerise** under high pressure and high temperature conditions and using a range of catalysts. In this process the individual alkene molecules, called **monomers**, bond together (using their π bonds) to form an **addition polymer**. For example, ethene, C_2H_4, forms polyethene in which the two electrons in the π bonds of the monomer (ethene) form σ (single) bonds with other ethene units, as shown in Figure 12.10.

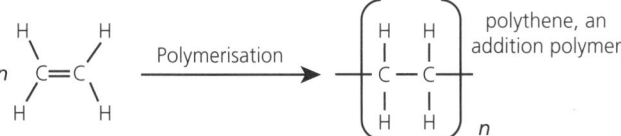

Figure 12.10 Polymerisation

Figure 12.11 shows how chloroethene (monomer) forms a polymer called polyvinylchloride (PVC).

> **Exam tip**
>
> In most polymers, there are no carbon–carbon double bonds. Therefore, polymers are fairly unreactive substances.

Figure 12.11 Making PVC

Polymers have many uses — film wrapping, carrier bags, bottles, kitchenware, shrink-wrap etc. However, disposal is a problem because many polymers do not biodegrade. Recycling poly(propene), for example, is a more cost-effective method than producing new polymer from crude oil. This is because energy costs are considerably less.

Now test yourself

4 Draw the structures of the major products expected when propene reacts with:
  (a) hydrogen bromide, HBr
  (b) bromine, Br_2
  (c) sulfuric acid, H_2SO_4
  (d) steam and an acid catalyst
5 Draw the structure of the polymer polypropene, showing three repeat units.

Answers on p. 104

Exam practice

1 (a) State what is observed when bromine water is added to (i) an alkene and (ii) an alkane. [2]
  (b) Name the mechanism for the reaction between an alkene and a halogen such as bromine. [1]
  (c) Draw the mechanism to show the reaction between propene and bromine. Take care when indicating the positions of any arrows in the mechanism. [4]
2 (a) Name the alkenes in Figure 12.12. [3]

molecule 1   molecule 2   molecule 3

Figure 12.12

  (b) Give the common molecular formula for each of these alkenes. [1]
  (c) How are all three molecules related? [1]
  (d) Explain which of the molecules is able to exist as E–Z isomers. [2]
  (e) Draw the structure of the major product formed when molecule 2 reacts with hydrogen bromide. Explain, using the mechanism of the reaction, why this is the major product. [3]
  (f) Draw structures of the repeat units in the polymers formed by:
     (i) molecule 2
     (ii) molecule 3 [2]

3 A student carried out an experiment to determine the number of C=C double bonds in a molecule of a cooking oil by measuring the volume of bromine water decolorised. The student followed these instructions:
- Use a dropping pipette to add 5 drops of oil to $5.0\,cm^3$ of inert organic solvent in a conical flask.
- Use a funnel to fill a burette with bromine water.
- Add bromine water from a burette to the solution in the conical flask and swirl the flask after each addition to measure the volume of bromine water that is decolorised. The student's results are shown in Table 12.1.

Table 12.1

Experiment	Volume of bromine water/cm³
1	39.40
2	43.50
3	41.20

(a) In a trial experiment, the student failed to fill the burette correctly so that the gap between the tap and the tip of the burette still contained air. Suggest what effect this would have on the measured volume of bromine water in this trial. Explain your answer. [2]

(b) Other than incorrect use of the burette, suggest a reason for the inconsistency in the student's results. [1]

(c) Outline how the student could improve this practical procedure to determine the number of C=C double bonds in a molecule of the oil so that more consistent results are obtained. [4]

(d) The oil has a density of $0.92\,g\,cm^{-3}$ and each of the 5 drops of oil has a volume of $5.0 \times 10^{-2}\,cm^3$. The approximate M_r of the oil is 885. The concentration of bromine water used was $2.0 \times 10^{-2}\,mol\,dm^{-3}$. Use these data and the results from experiment 1 to deduce the number of C=C double bonds in a molecule of the oil. Show your working. [5]

Answers and quick quiz 12 online

ONLINE ☐

Summary

You should now have an understanding of:
- what is meant by the term 'unsaturated' when applied to alkenes
- the structure of a carbon–carbon double bond and how free rotation is restricted
- the existence of E–Z isomerism
- the reactions of alkenes with HBr, H_2SO_4 and Br_2

- how two products are possible when HBr reacts with an unsymmetrical alkene, and why one may be preferred over the other
- how an alcohol is produced industrially by the reaction of an alkene with steam in the presence of an acid catalyst
- how alkenes polymerise to form addition polymers.

13 Alcohols

Naming alcohols

Number of carbon atoms

REVISED

Alcohols are named according to the number of carbon atoms in their molecules, and also the position of the hydroxyl group, OH.

The molecules in Figure 13.1 are called pentan-1-ol, pentan-2-ol and 2-methylbutan-2-ol respectively.

> **Alcohols** are hydrocarbons that have one or more of their hydrogen atoms replaced by a hydroxyl group (–OH).

Figure 13.1 Isomeric alcohols

Ethanol production

Ethanol, C_2H_5OH, is a very useful substance because it is a fuel that burns to release heat energy:

$$C_2H_5OH(l) + 3O_2(g) \rightarrow 2CO_2(g) + 3H_2O(l)$$

There are two very different ways of making ethanol: **fermentation of sugars** and **hydration of ethene**.

Fermentation of sugars

REVISED

Sugars are obtained from crops such as sugar cane, sugar beet, corn, rice and maize. Naturally occurring starches (in corn, rice and maize) form sugars by enzyme-controlled processes and, once the sugars are formed, fermentation takes place in the presence of enzymes in yeast:

$$C_6H_{12}O_6(aq) \rightarrow 2C_2H_5OH(aq) + 2CO_2(g)$$

Ethanol formed in this way is called a **biofuel** because it is formed from **renewable** plants (those that can be grown again or replenished).

> **Fermentation** is the process in which microorganisms convert one substance into another, normally in the *absence of air*.

The advantages of this process are as follows:
- Sugars come from **renewable resources**.
- The energy requirements are low (enzymes operate best at room or body temperature).
- The process is carbon-neutral — any carbon dioxide produced is removed from the air by photosynthesis in the original plant so, overall, there has been no net change in carbon dioxide levels.

Disadvantages include the following:
- The ethanol formed is in the form of an aqueous solution — therefore, heat energy is needed for fractional distillation; producing this energy is expensive and not carbon-neutral.

> **Exam tip**
>
> Photosynthesis involves the removal of carbon dioxide from the air; fermentation produces carbon dioxide. So, carbon-neutral fuels have zero effect on carbon dioxide levels.

- The process is slow — it takes several days for the ethanol concentration to reach its limit of approximately 16% by volume.
- Renewable crops require huge surface areas of land to grow, and the machinery and people-power required in harvesting these crops can be significant.

Hydration of ethene

This reaction was discussed in Chapter 12 (page 87).

Ethene can be hydrated in the presence of phosphoric(v) to form ethanol at 300°C and a pressure of 60–70 kPa (Figure 13.2).

Figure 13.2

The advantages of this method are as follows:
- The ethanol is pure, so no separation is required afterwards.
- The rate of reaction is high, so the ethanol is formed quickly.
- The process is continuous, so ethene and steam can be added automatically without any costly breaks in production or use of manpower.

Disadvantages include the following:
- Ethene is obtained from the cracking of crude oil, and cracking requires huge energy reserves.
- Crude oil is a non-renewable resource, so once the crude oil is used it cannot be replenished or reformed.
- The process of hydration requires a high temperature (300°C) and high pressure (60–70 atm) — both of which have considerable energy and cost implications.

> **Exam tip**
>
> Make sure that you know the disadvantages and advantages of the two methods of making ethanol, including the environmental issues.

Classification of alcohols

Alcohols are sorted into groups (Figure 13.3) according to how many alkyl groups are attached to the carbon atom covalently bonded to the hydroxyl group.

Figure 13.3 Primary, secondary and tertiary alcohols

The class of alcohol determines the type of reaction it may undergo — particularly when being oxidised.

Oxidation of alcohols

Alcohols can be oxidised using acidified potassium dichromate(vi) as the oxidising agent. The product molecule formed depends on the class of the original alcohol.

Primary alcohols

Primary alcohols are oxidised to form **aldehydes** and then **carboxylic acids**. For example, ethanol is oxidised in the first stage to form **ethanal**, and then this is oxidised to form **ethanoic acid** — Figures 13.4 and 13.5 show the convenient use of '[O]' to represent the oxidising agent.

Figure 13.4 Oxidation of primary alcohols

During these reactions the orange dichromate(vi) ions are **reduced** and turn dark green. The alcohol is **oxidised**. These reactions are therefore **redox reactions**.
- Aldehydes are normally removed by **distillation** (to prevent further oxidation).

Secondary alcohols

As shown in Figure 13.5, secondary alcohols are oxidised to form **ketones**.

Figure 13.5 Oxidation of secondary alcohols

- Carboxylic acids are formed in a process involving **reflux**. A secondary alcohol and acidified potassium dichromate(vi) are normally **refluxed** to ensure that the reaction goes to completion.

> **Exam tip**
>
> The symbol [O] represents the oxidising agent and is used to balance oxidation equations such as those shown. You should treat it as a normal element symbol, and make sure the oxygens balance.

Tertiary alcohols

Tertiary alcohols cannot be oxidised using acidified potassium dichromate(vi) as an oxidising agent. So no reaction occurs and the acidified potassium dichromate(vi) stays orange.

Now test yourself

1 Draw the displayed formula of pentan-1-ol.
2 Give the structures and names of the products formed when pentan-1-ol is oxidised using acidified potassium dichromate(vi).

Answers on p. 104

Aldehydes and ketones

Aldehydes and ketones are called **carbonyl compounds** because they contain the carbonyl group. The functional groups present in aldehydes and ketones are shown in Figure 13.6 ('R' and 'R¹' represent alkyl groups) and some specific molecules in Figure 13.7.

Figure 13.6 Functional groups present in aldehydes and ketones

ethanal, CH_3CHO

propanone, CH_3COCH_3

propanal, C_2H_5CHO

pentan-3-one, $CH_3CH_2COCH_2CH_3$

Figure 13.7 Examples of aldehydes and ketones

Distinguishing aldehydes from ketones

REVISED

Tollens' reagent

Aldehydes and ketones can be distinguished from one another using **Tollens' reagent**, which is formed by mixing ammonia with silver nitrate solution.

In this reaction, ketones show no reaction but aldehydes form a **silver mirror** on the inside of the test tube — the silver ions are **reduced**.

$$Ag^+(aq) + e^- \rightarrow Ag(s)$$

and the aldehyde is **oxidised** to a carboxylic acid. Using ethanal as an example:

$$CH_3CHO + [O] \rightarrow CH_3COOH$$

Fehling's solution

In this test, the aldehyde reduces copper(II) ions and an **orange-brown precipitate** of copper(I) oxide is formed. Ketones show no reaction.

> **Typical mistake**
>
> Many students focus on the reduction of the silver ion when using Tollens' reagent. However, don't forget that the aldehyde has formed a carboxylic acid in the reaction too.

Elimination

Dehydration reactions

REVISED

Alcohols can be dehydrated using concentrated sulfuric acid (as a catalyst) to form an alkene. For example, propan-1-ol can be dehydrated to form propene:

$$CH_3CH_2CH_2OH \rightarrow CH_3CH=CH_2 + H_2O$$

Dehydration reactions can be used as a possible route for synthesising polymers from alcohols — for example, ethanol → ethene → polyethene.

So polymers could be made starting from sugars, thus avoiding the reliance on crude oil as the original source of carbon.

Now test yourself

3 Draw the structures of butanone and butanal.
4 Describe a chemical test to distinguish butanone from butanal.

Answers on p. 104

Exam practice

1 A polymer such as polyethene could be synthesised from glucose using this route:

$$C_6H_{12}O_6 \text{ (glucose)} \xrightarrow{\text{step 1}} C_2H_5OH \xrightarrow{\text{step 2}} C_2H_4 \xrightarrow{\text{step 3}} \text{polyethene}$$

(a) Give the reagents and conditions required for each stage of the route above. [6]
(b) Give the name of the chemical process in each step. [3]
(c) Draw the repeat unit in polythene. [1]

2 Substance A in Figure 13.8 can be synthesised from an alcohol under appropriate conditions.

$$CH_3-CH_2-CH-C\overset{\displaystyle O}{\underset{\displaystyle H}{}}$$
$$\overset{|}{CH_3}$$

Figure 13.8

(a) Name molecule A. [1]
(b) Draw the structure of an alcohol that, when oxidised, would produce molecule A. [1]
(c) Give the name of the reagent(s) used to form A from the alcohol. [1]

3 Tollens' reagent is added to a sample of A and the resulting solution heated.
(a) State what would be observed in the reaction. [1]
(b) Draw the structure of the organic molecule formed in the reaction. [1]

4 Compound J, known as leaf alcohol, has the structural formula $CH_3CH_2CH=CHCH_2CH_2OH$ and is produced in small quantities by many green plants. The E-isomer of J is responsible for the smell of freshly cut grass.
(a) Give the structure of the E-isomer of J. [1]
(b) Give the skeletal formula of the organic product formed when J is dehydrated using concentrated sulfuric acid. [1]
(c) Another structural isomer of J is shown in Figure 13.9.

$$\underset{CH_3}{\overset{CH_3CH_2}{}}C=C\underset{H}{\overset{CH_2OH}{}}$$

Figure 13.9

Explain how the Cahn-Ingold-Prelog (CIP) priority rules can be used to deduce the full IUPAC name of this compound. [6]

Answers and quick quiz 13 online

Summary

You should now have an understanding of:
- the molecular structure of alcohols and their key functional group
- how to name simple alcohols
- how ethanol can be made on an industrial scale, either by fermentation or hydration, and the advantages and disadvantages of each process

- how to classify alcohols as primary, secondary or tertiary
- the oxidation of alcohols of different classes using acidified potassium dichromate(VI)
- Tollens' reagent and how it is used to distinguish between aldehydes and ketones
- elimination reactions, in which alkenes are made from alcohols

14 Organic analysis

Several modern analytical techniques are useful when determining the structures of molecules.

Identification of functional groups by test-tube reactions

You may be asked to carry out simple chemical tests that would enable you to distinguish between well-known functional groups, for example alkenes, alcohols, carboxylic acids, aldehydes and ketones. These chemical tests are already mentioned in earlier chapters, but for convenience, they are summarised in Table 14.1.

Table 14.1

Functional group being tested	Test being carried out	Positive identification
Alkenes $\text{C}=\text{C}$	Bromine water, $Br_2(aq)$, is added to the sample	An orange solution will turn colourless
Alcohols $R-O-H$	Add acidified potassium dichromate(VI) and warm the mixture gently	(a) Primary and secondary alcohol — an orange solution will turn green (b) Tertiary alcohol — no reaction takes place, so the solution stays orange
Carboxylic acids $R-\overset{O}{\underset{}{C}}-O-H$	Test as a typical acid and add some sodium carbonate, Na_2CO_3, either as a solid or solution	Fizzing will occur and the gas can be bubbled through limewater, which goes milky
Aldehydes $R-\overset{O}{\underset{}{C}}-H$	Add either (a) ammoniacal silver nitrate solution or (b) Fehling's solution, and warm in a water bath	(a) A silver mirror will form (b) A blue solution will form a brown/orange/red precipitate

Now test yourself

TESTED

1 What are the systematic names of the molecules in Figure 14.1?

Figure 14.1

2 Describe a chemical test that would enable you to distinguish between the molecules in Figure 14.1.
3 Draw the structures of, and name, the organic products formed in these two tests.

Answers on p. 104

Mass spectrometry

Mass spectrometry instrumentation was discussed earlier in Chapter 1 where it was used for analysing elements. It is also very useful when analysing organic compounds.

It is possible to measure with great precision the mass of a **molecular ion** if the relative isotopic masses to four decimal places are used. For example:

$^1H = 1.0078$ $^{12}C = 12.0000$ $^{14}N = 14.0031$ $^{16}O = 15.9949$

For example, the two organic compounds propane (C_3H_8) and ethanal (CH_3CHO) both have relative molecular mass $M_r = 44$ to the nearest whole number. Using a high-resolution mass spectrometer, two molecular ion peaks with the following more precise m/z values are obtained:

$C_3H_8 = 44.0624$ $CH_3CHO = 44.0261$

When analysing samples, it is therefore possible to deduce the molecular formula of a compound by measuring its precise relative molecular mass. The relative molecular mass of a compound is given by the peak with the highest m/z value.

A computer database can hold the relative molecular masses of thousands of organic molecules, measured to a high level of accuracy; a sample under test can then be compared to other spectra and its identity determined.

> A **molecular ion** is the original molecule that has lost one electron, M^+. Its mass will be virtually the same as the molecule being tested, because an electron has negligible mass.

Infrared spectroscopy

Atoms in covalent bonds are **vibrating** about a mean position. The frequency of the vibration depends on the masses of the atoms in the bond — the greater the mass of the atoms, the slower the vibrations.

Vibrational frequency

REVISED

The frequency of such a vibration can be quoted in **wavenumbers** — the number of waves in 1 cm. One particular bond will vibrate at a certain wavenumber. However, just as the energy of a particular covalent bond will vary slightly in different compounds, the frequency of vibration also varies, so values are usually quoted as a range, as in Table 14.2.

Table 14.2 Typical wavenumbers in infrared spectra

Bond	Wavenumber/cm^{-1}
C–H in alkanes	2850–2960
C–C	750–1100
C–O	1000–1300
O–H in carboxylic acids	2500–3000
C=O	1680–1750
O–H in hydrogen-bonded alcohols	3230–3550 (broad adsorption)
C–N in amines	1180–1360
C–Cl	600–800
C–Br	500–600

Figure 14.2 shows the displayed formula for ethyl ethanoate, $CH_3COOC_2H_5$.

Notice the bonds present in this compound: C–H, C=O, C–O and C–C. These will vibrate at certain wavenumbers. For example, the C=O bond is expected to vibrate at $1743\,cm^{-1}$ (Figure 14.3).

$$CH_3 \!-\! \underset{\underset{O}{\|}}{C} \!-\! O \!-\! CH_2 \!-\! CH_3$$

Figure 14.2 Ethyl ethanoate

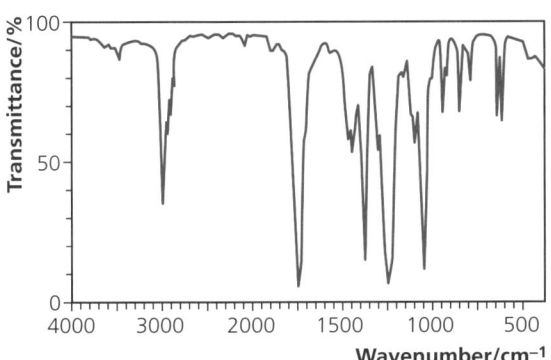

Figure 14.3 The infrared spectrum for ethyl ethanoate

The fingerprint region

The peaks below $1500\,cm^{-1}$ in the spectrum are used collectively as a fingerprint region. This characteristic arrangement of peaks is unique to the compound, just as a fingerprint is unique to a person. Therefore, by comparing the fingerprint region of an unknown compound with many on a computer database, the identity of the compound can be deduced.

It is possible to detect impurities in a compound because these may give rise to absorptions that would not be expected for that compound.

Some molecules in the atmosphere absorb infrared radiation and contribute towards global warming. This is because the natural frequency of the bond vibration in molecules such as CO_2 or H_2O coincides exactly with the frequency of the infrared radiation. The same process takes place when a sample is put into an infrared spectrometer.

Now test yourself

TESTED ☐

4 Draw the structure of propan-1-ol.
5 Write down the bonds present in propan-1-ol.
6 Give the wavenumbers of the main peaks expected in the infrared spectrum of this compound.
7 A small absorption is observed at a wavenumber of $1720\,cm^{-1}$. What does this suggest about the sample?

Answers on p. 104

Exam practice

1 In an experiment to prepare a sample of ethanal (CH_3CHO), ethanol (C_2H_5OH) is reacted with acidified potassium dichromate(vi) and the reaction mixture is distilled. Infrared spectra are obtained for ethanol and ethanal (Figure 14.4).

Infrared spectrum for ethanol   Infrared spectrum for ethanal

Figure 14.4

(a) Indicate the bonds that give rise to these absorptions:
   (i) in the ethanol spectrum at 3400 cm⁻¹
   (ii) in the ethanal spectrum at 1720 cm⁻¹   [2]

(b) Write an equation to show the oxidation of ethanol to form ethanal, using [O] to represent the oxidising agent.   [1]

(c) Explain why the absorption at 3400 cm⁻¹ in the ethanol spectrum does not appear in the spectrum for ethanal.   [1]

(d) The reaction mixture from the experiment containing ethanal was left for several days, and another infrared spectrum taken. It was observed that a new absorption was present between 2500 cm⁻¹ and 3000 cm⁻¹. Explain this observation.   [2]

2 When cyclohexanol is heated with concentrated sulfuric acid, a reaction occurs and a new product is formed. The infrared spectrum for the new compound is shown in Figure 14.5.

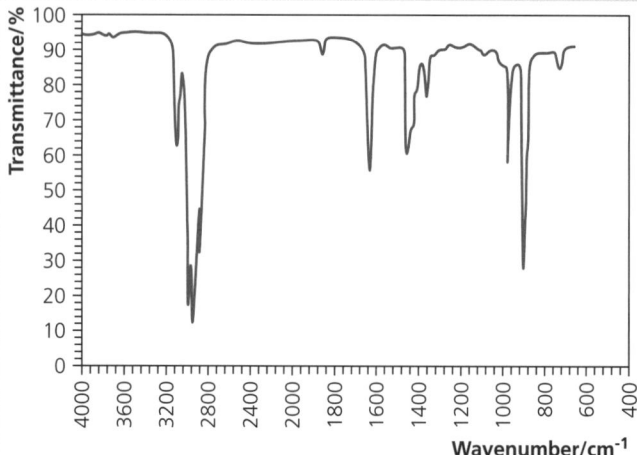

Figure 14.5

Exam practice answers and quick quizzes at **www.hoddereducation.co.uk/myrevisionnotes**

(a) Use the data in Table 14.3 to explain how the spectrum can indicate that cyclohexanol is no longer present. [1]

Table 14.3 Infrared absorption data

Bond	Wavenumber/cm⁻¹
C–H	2850–3300
C–C	750–1100
C=C	1620–1680
C=O	1680–1750
C–O	1000–1300
O–H (alcohols)	3230–3550
O–H (acids)	2500–3000

(b) Using the spectrum, identify the product of the reaction, giving reasons for your choice. [2]
(c) Indicate how high-resolution mass spectrometry can be used to identify the product of this reaction. [1]

3 Give two differences between the infrared spectrum of a carboxylic acid and that of an alcohol other than in their fingerprint regions. [2]

Answers and quick quiz 14 online

ONLINE

Summary

You should now have an understanding of:
- how mass spectrometry can be used to identify a substance by measuring an accurate value for the mass of the molecular ion
- how infrared spectroscopy works by measuring characteristic vibrational frequencies in a molecule
- how infrared spectroscopy can be used to identify the main bonds in a molecule

- the 'fingerprint region' in the infrared spectrum and its importance when identifying a compound
- global warming in terms of molecular vibrations — the same process that takes place when measuring the infrared spectrum of a compound

Now test yourself answers

Chapter 1

1 (a) 9 protons, 10 neutrons, 9 electrons
  (b) 34 protons, 40 neutrons, 34 electrons
  (c) 22 protons, 26 neutrons, 20 electrons
  (d) 35 protons, 44 neutrons, 36 electrons

2 relative atomic mass of krypton = $\left(\dfrac{0.35}{100} \times 78\right)$ +
$\left(\dfrac{2.3}{100} \times 80\right) + \left(\dfrac{11.6}{100} \times 82\right) + \left(\dfrac{11.5}{100} \times 83\right) + \left(\dfrac{56.9}{100} \times 84\right)$ +
$\left(\dfrac{17.4}{100} \times 86\right)$
= 83.93 (no units)

3 Let y = % of ^{10}B, then % of ^{11}B = 100 − y
Therefore, $\left(\dfrac{y}{100} \times 10\right) + \left(\dfrac{100 - y}{100} \times 11\right) = 10.8$
So, $0.1y + 11 - \left(\dfrac{11}{100}\,y\right) = 10.8$
This gives 0.2 = 0.01y, so y = 20%, so ^{10}B = 20% and ^{11}B = 80%

4 (a) beryllium: $1s^2, 2s^2$; magnesium: $1s^2, 2s^2, 2p^6, 3s^2$; calcium: $1s^2, 2s^2, 2p^6, 3s^2, 3p^6, 4s^2$
  (b) The number of electrons in the +3 ion is 10, so the atomic number is 10 + 3 = 13.

5 (a)

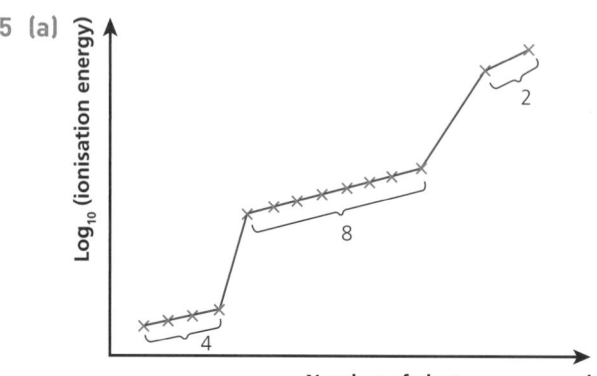

  (b) $P^{3+}(g) \rightarrow P^{4+}(g) + e^-$

Chapter 2

1 amount of Ca = $\dfrac{1.00}{40.1}$ = 0.0249 mol
amount of Cl = $\dfrac{1.77}{35.5}$ = 0.0500 mol
ratio is 1 : 2; empirical formula is $CaCl_2$

2 amount of calcium = $\dfrac{0.210}{40.1}$ = 5.24 × 10^{-3}
amount of silicon = $\dfrac{0.147}{28.1}$ = 5.23 × 10^{-3} mol

amount of oxygen = $\dfrac{0.252}{16.0}$ = 0.0158 mol
ratio is 1 : 1 : 3; empirical formula is $CaSiO_3$

3 (a) Assuming a total mass of 100 g:
  amount of nitrogen = $\dfrac{30.4}{14.0}$ = 2.17 mol
  amount of oxygen = $\dfrac{100 - 30.4}{16.0}$ = 4.35 mol
  ratio is 1 : 2; empirical formula is NO_2
  (b) Because the relative molecular mass is 92, twice the empirical formula is required; the molecular formula is N_2O_4.

4 (a) The molecular formula of caffeine is $C_8H_{10}N_4O_2$.
  (b) (i) Relative molecular mass = (8 × 12.0) + (10 × 1.0) + (4 × 14.0) + (2 × 16.0) = 194
      Given that the mass of caffeine is 5.60 × 10^{-3} g:
      amount present in mol = $\dfrac{5.60 \times 10^{-3}}{194}$
      = 2.89 × 10^{-5} mol
      number of molecules this represents = 2.89 × 10^{-5} × 6.0 × 10^{23} = 1.73 × 10^{19}
  (ii) Each caffeine molecule consists of eight carbon atoms. So when 1.73 × 10^{19} caffeine molecules are completely combusted, the number of carbon dioxide molecules formed will be (8 × 1.73 × 10^{19}), or 1.39 × 10^{20} molecules.

5 Using $pV = nRT$:
  p × 0.0330 = 0.905 × 8.31 × (200 + 273)
  pressure = 1.08 × 10^5 Pa

6 amount of Mg = $\dfrac{2.00}{24.3}$ = 0.0823 mol
  amount of hydrogen = 0.0823 mol
  volume of hydrogen = $\dfrac{nRT}{p}$ = $\dfrac{0.0823 \times 8.31 \times 298}{100\,000}$
  = 0.00204 m^3 or 2.04 dm^3

7 ratio of nitrogen to hydrogen is 1 : 3
  volume of hydrogen required = 150 cm^3 × 3 = 450 cm^3

8 amount of H_2O_2 dissolved = $\dfrac{100}{1000}$ × 0.500 = 0.0500 mol
  amount of oxygen formed = $\dfrac{0.0500}{2}$ = 0.0250 mol
  volume = $\dfrac{nRT}{p}$ = $\dfrac{0.0250 \times 8.31 \times 298}{100\,000}$ = 0.619 dm^3

9 Using moles dissolved = $\frac{\text{volume (cm}^3)}{1000\,\text{cm}^3} \times$ concentration (in mol dm^3):

  (a) amount dissolved = $\frac{10.0}{1000} \times 0.200\,\text{mol dm}^{-3}$
      = $2.00 \times 10^{-3}\,\text{mol NaOH}$

  (b) amount dissolved = $\frac{250}{1000} \times 1.20\,\text{mol dm}^{-3}$
      = $0.300\,\text{mol HNO}_3$

10 amount of dissolved HCl = $\frac{20.0}{1000} \times 0.900$
    = $0.0180\,\text{mol}$

  amount of NaOH reacting is 0.0180 mol

  So volume reacting = $0.018 \times \frac{1000}{0.0500} = 360\,\text{cm}^3$

11 atom economy = $\left(\frac{50.5}{50.5 + 36.5}\right) \times 100 = 58.0\%$

12 (a) NaF

  (b) K$_2$SO$_4$

  (c) Al(OH)$_3$

13 $2\text{Al(s)} + 3\text{CuSO}_4\text{(aq)} \rightarrow \text{Al}_2\text{(SO}_4)_3\text{(aq)} + 3\text{Cu(s)}$

14 $\text{KOH(aq)} + \text{HCl(aq)} \rightarrow \text{KCl(aq)} + \text{H}_2\text{O(l)}$
  $\text{H}^+\text{(aq)} + \text{OH}^-\text{(aq)} \rightarrow \text{H}_2\text{O(l)}$

Chapter 3

1 (a)

     Mg^{2+} O^{2-}

  (b)

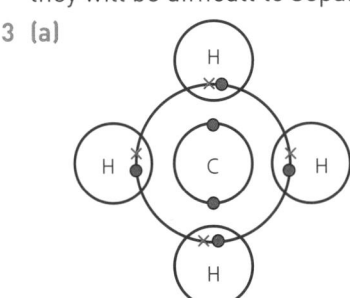

     Na$^+$ O^{2-}

2 Lithium fluoride has a giant ionic lattice structure; there will be oppositely charged ions — Li$^+$ and F$^-$; these will be attracted to each other strongly by electrostatic forces; this means that they will be difficult to separate.

3 (a)

(b)

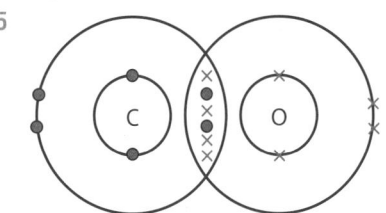

4 Methane is simple covalent; this means that the individual molecules will be relatively easy to separate as the substance melts.

5

6 Hydrogen and fluorine have very different electronegativities; this results in a dipole forming in HF with the bonded electrons closer to the fluorine end of the molecule. In hydrogen, the atoms are identical; so their electronegativities will be the same; H$_2$ will therefore be a non-polar molecule.

7

8 As the group is descended, molecules contain more electrons; therefore, there will be greater van der Waals forces; this means that it will be more difficult to separate the halogen molecules at the bottom of the group.

9 NaF has a giant ionic lattice structure whereas F$_2$ is simple covalent; in NaF the oppositely charged ions will be difficult to separate because they are electrostatically attracted; in F$_2$ the individual molecules are easy to separate; so fluorine has a lower melting point.

10 (a) tetrahedral

(b) trigonal planar

(c) octahedral

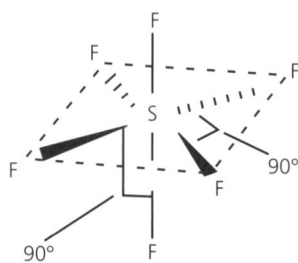

Chapter 4

1 Using $q = mc\Delta T$:

$q = 25.0 \times 4.18 \times 11.4 = 1191\,J = 1.19\,kJ$

amount of zinc used $= \dfrac{0.95}{65.4} = 0.0145\,mol$

enthalpy change $= \dfrac{1.19\,kJ}{0.0145\,mol} = -82.1\,kJ\,mol^{-1}$

2 $q = mc\Delta T$

$q = 100 \times 4.18 \times (25.0 - 17.0) = 3344\,J = 3.34\,kJ$

0.16 g of methanol (CH_3OH) is $\dfrac{0.16}{32.0}$ mol, i.e. 5.00×10^{-3} mol

enthalpy change $= \dfrac{3.34\,kJ}{5.00 \times 10^{-3}} = -668\,kJ\,mol^{-1}$

3 (a) $C(s) + O_2(g) \rightarrow CO_2(g)$

(b) $6C(s) + 7H_2(g) \rightarrow C_6H_{14}(l)$

4 $\Delta H = \Sigma\Delta_f H(\text{products}) - \Sigma\Delta_f H(\text{reactants}) = (4 \times -1279) - [-2984.0 + (6 \times -285.8)] = -5116 - (-4698.8) = -417.2\,kJ\,mol^{-1}$

5 $\Delta_f H(\text{propane}) = (3 \times -393.5) + (4 \times -285.8) - (-2220.0) = -1180.5 - 1143.2 + 2220.0 = -103.7\,kJ\,mol^{-1}$

6 ΔH = energy required to break bonds – energy released on forming new bonds = $[409 + (2 \times 388) + 436)] - [163 + (4 \times 388)] = 1621 - 1715 = -94\,kJ\,mol^{-1}$

Chapter 5

1 As temperature increases, particles move with a higher kinetic energy; and a greater proportion have an energy that exceeds the activation energy; so there will be more effective collisions per unit time; and the rate increases.

2 As the concentration increases, the number of ions per unit volume also increases; there will be more collisions per unit time; and the rate of reaction increases.

3 Manganese(IV) oxide is a catalyst for the decomposition of hydrogen peroxide to form water and oxygen. The catalyst provides an alternative reaction pathway, which is faster because it has a lower activation energy.

Chapter 6

1 (a) $K_c = \dfrac{[NH_3(g)]^2}{[N_2(g)]\,[H_2(g)]^3}$

(b) $K_c = \dfrac{[HI(g)]^2}{[H_2(g)]\,[I_2(g)]}$

(c) $K_c = \dfrac{[NO(g)]^2}{[N_2(g)]\,[O_2(g)]}$

2 (a) When the temperature is increased, the equilibrium position shifts to the left-hand side by using its endothermic route.

(b) As temperature increases, the rate of reaction will always increase; more molecules have an energy that exceeds the activation energy; there will be more effective collisions taking place per unit time; and the rate will increase.

(c) $K_c = \dfrac{[N_2O_4(g)]}{[NO_2(g)]^2}$

3

	Equilibrium position	Rate at which equilibrium is attained
Total pressure is decreased	Shifts to the right-hand side	Increases
Temperature is increased	Shifts to the left-hand side	Increases
A catalyst is added	No change	Increases

Chapter 7

1 (a) +3

(b) +1

(c) +4

(d) +6

(e) +6

(f) +5

(g) +6

2 (a) cobalt(III) chloride

(b) sodium chlorate(I)

(c) titanium(IV) chloride

(d) sodium ferrate(VI)

(e) sulfuric(VI) acid

(f) iodate(V) ion

(g) manganate(VI) ion

3 oxidising agent: oxygen gas, O_2; reducing agent: SO_2

4 Pb: +4 to +2; Pb(IV) is the oxidising agent

Cl: –1 to 0; Cl⁻ is the reducing agent (some Cl⁻ is unchanged)

5 (a) $Zn(s) \rightarrow Zn^{2+}(aq) + 2e^-$

$Fe^{2+}(aq) + 2e^- \rightarrow Fe(s)$

(b) $2Al(s) \rightarrow 2Al^{3+}(aq) + 6e^-$

$3Cu^{2+}(aq) + 6e^- \rightarrow 3Cu(s)$

Chapter 8

1 p block

2 p block

3 (a) Magnesium atoms have 12 protons in the nucleus; sodium has 11; both have the same number of energy levels or shells. The outer electrons in magnesium will experience a stronger attraction; there will be a contraction in size, giving a smaller atomic radius.

(b) In aluminium, the electron being removed comes from a 3p orbital, which is slightly further away from the nucleus than the 3s orbital in magnesium from which its electron is removed; there is also slightly more shielding; so the electron being removed from an aluminium atom is attracted more weakly; the first ionisation energy will be lower.

(c) Both are simple covalent; but sulfur consists of S_8 molecules whereas chlorine consists of Cl_2 molecules; S_8 molecules have more electrons; and the van der Waals forces are greater; so its boiling point will be higher.

Chapter 9

1 $Ca(s) + 2H_2O(l) \rightarrow Ca(OH)_2(aq) + H_2(g)$

Bubbles would be observed; calcium metal (a light-grey solid) would eventually dissolve to form a white suspension in water.

2 Add barium chloride solution and hydrochloric acid to separate solutions of sodium sulfate and sodium nitrate; a white precipitate forms with sodium sulfate; there is no reaction with sodium nitrate.

3 Chlorine has fewer electron energy levels compared with iodine; so the added electron will be closer to the nucleus in the chlorine atom; and the electrostatic attraction will be greater; so chlorine will be the more powerful oxidising agent.

4 (a) $Br_2(aq) + 2NaI(aq) \rightarrow 2NaBr(aq) + I_2(aq)$ or $Br_2(aq) + 2I^-(aq) \rightarrow 2Br^-(aq) + I_2(aq)$

(b) Bromine has been reduced; iodide ions have been oxidised.

5 $KF(s) + H_2SO_4(l) \rightarrow KHSO_4(s) + HF(g)$

6 (a) H_2S: –2; SO_2: +4; S: 0

(b) $6HI(g) + H_2SO_4(l) \rightarrow 3I_2(s) + S(s) + 4H_2O(l)$

7 To a solution of each salt; add dilute nitric acid and then silver nitrate solution; a white precipitate of AgCl forms with lithium chloride; and a yellow precipitate of AgI forms with lithium iodide.

$Ag^+(aq) + Cl^-(aq) \rightarrow AgCl(s)$

$Ag^+(aq) + I^-(aq) \rightarrow AgI(s)$

8 (a) chlorine: purifying drinking water; sodium chlorate(I): bleach

(b) water and chlorine gas

Chapter 10

1 displayed formula:

H—C—C—C—C—C—C—H (with H atoms above and below each carbon)

structural formula: $CH_3(CH_2)_4CH_3$

molecular formula: C_6H_{14}

empirical formula, C_3H_7

2 n-pentane, 2-methylbutane and 2,2-dimethylpropane

3 $C_9H_{20}(g) \rightarrow C_2H_4(g) + C_7H_{16}(g)$

4 $350\,cm^3$

5 $CH_4(g) + \frac{3}{2}O_2(g) \rightarrow CO(g) + 2H_2O(l)$

6 Oxides of nitrogen, carbon monoxide; both can be removed using a catalytic converter.

Chapter 11

1 (a) CFCs produce chlorine radicals in the presence of ultraviolet light; these then attack ozone molecules.

(b) A particle (atom, molecule or ion); with one or more unpaired electrons.

(c) $Cl\bullet + O_3 \rightarrow ClO\bullet + O_2$; then $ClO\bullet + O_3 \rightarrow 2O_2 + Cl\bullet$

2 (a) $C_2H_6(g) + Br_2(g) \rightarrow C_2H_5Br(l) + HBr(g)$

(b) free-radical substitution

(c) Initiation: $Br_2 \rightarrow 2Br\bullet$

Propagation: bromine radicals react with ethane molecules to form new radicals and molecules:

$C_2H_6 + Br\bullet \rightarrow HBr + \bullet C_2H_5$ then: $\bullet C_2H_5 + Br_2 \rightarrow C_2H_5Br + Br\bullet$

Termination: radicals react with each other to form molecules:

$\bullet C_2H_5 + Br\bullet \rightarrow C_2H_5Br$ or $\bullet C_2H_5 + \bullet C_2H_5 \rightarrow C_4H_{10}$

Chapter 12

1

Z-pent-2-ene   E-pent-2-ene

2 As written, from left to right, *E* (*trans*), *Z* (*cis*), *E* (*trans*), *Z* (*cis*), *Z* (*cis*), *E* (*trans*).

3 (a)

(b)

or

(c) The tertiary carbocation:

(d)

4 (a)

(b)

(c)

(d)

5

Chapter 13

1

2

pentanal   pentanoic acid

3

butanone   butanal

4 Silver nitrate and ammonia solution (Tollens' reagent); this is heated separately with both substances; butanal will form a silver mirror; butanone will not.

Chapter 14

1 propanoic acid and propan-2-ol

2 Add sodium carbonate, Na_2CO_3, to each sample; propanoic acid would fizz and produce carbon dioxide, which can be positively tested using limewater; propan-2-ol results in no reaction.

or

Add acidified potassium dichromate(VI) solution to each compound and warm gently; propan-2-ol will result in an orange solution turning green; no reaction takes place with propanoic acid.

3

Sodium propanoate

or

Propanone

4

5 C–C; C–H; C–O; O–H

6 likely wavenumbers: $3000–3300\,cm^{-1}$ (broad) for the OH; $1000–1300\,cm^{-1}$ for the C–O

7 Likely to be due to a C=O bond; the sample therefore contains an impurity such as propanal or propanoic acid; formed by the oxidation of propan-1-ol.